PUBLIC POLICY AND AGRICULTURAL TECHNOLOGY

POLICY STUDIES ORGANIZATION SERIES

General Editor: Stuart S. Nagel, Professor of Political Science, University of Illinois at Urbana-Champaign

Sheldon H. Danziger and Kent E. Portney (*editors*)
THE DISTRIBUTIONAL IMPACTS OF PUBLIC POLICIES

Don F. Hadwiger and William P. Browne (*editors*)
PUBLIC POLICY AND AGRICULTURAL TECHNOLOGY: Adversity Despite Achievement

Richard C. Hula (*editor*)
MARKET-BASED PUBLIC POLICY

Rita Mae Kelly (*editor*)
PROMOTING PRODUCTIVITY IN THE PUBLIC SECTOR: Problems, Strategies and Prospects

Fred Lazin, Samuel Aroni and Yehuda Gradus (*editors*)
DEVELOPING AREAS AND PUBLIC POLICY

J. David Roessner (*editor*)
GOVERNMENT INNOVATION POLICY: Design, Implementation, Evaluation

Public Policy and Agricultural Technology

Adversity Despite Achievement

Edited by
Don F. Hadwiger
Professor of Political Science
Iowa State University

and

William P. Browne
Professor of Political Science
Central Michigan University

MACMILLAN
PRESS in association with the
POLICY STUDIES ORGANIZATION

First published 1987

Published by
THE MACMILLAN PRESS LTD
Houndmills, Basingstoke, Hampshire RG21 2XS
and London
Companies and representatives
throughout the world

Printed in Hong Kong

British Library Cataloguing in Publication Data
Public policy and agricultural technology:
adversity despite achievement.—(Policy
Studies Organization)
1. Agricultural—Research—Political
aspects—United States
I. Hadwiger, Don F. II. Browne, William P.
III. Series
630'.727073 S541
ISBN 0–333–44192–3

Contents

Preface vii

Notes on the Contributors x

PART I AGRICULTURAL RESEARCH IN A POLICY SETTING

1 Introduction 3
Don F. Hadwiger and William P. Browne

2 Constituents and Constituencies: An Overview of the History of Public Agricultural Research Institutions in America 15
Alan I. Marcus

PART II THINKING ABOUT AGRICULTURAL AND RESEARCH ALTERNATIVES

3 Inefficiency and Structural Adjustment in American Agriculture: Who Will Quit and Why? 33
Carlisle Ford Runge

4 Moving from Yesterday's Agricultural Technology: Alternative Farming Systems in Perspective 53
I. Garth Youngberg

PART III CURRENT POLITICAL ISSUES AND CONFLICT

5 Political Support for National and International Public Research 67
Hemchandra Gajbhiye and Don F. Hadwiger

6 An Emerging Opposition? Agricultural Interests and Federal Research Policy 81
William P. Browne

PART IV THE PROSPECTS FOR AGENDA CHANGE

7 Toward a New Covenant for Agricultural Academe 93
J. Patrick Madden

8 Biotechnology and International Development: Prospects for Overcoming Dependence in the Information Age 109
Frederick H. Buttel and Martin Kenney

Author Index 122
Subject Index 125

Preface

This book was written at an exceptionally dramatic and paradoxical time in the history of agricultural research. Nations throughout the world are on the verge of rapidly expanding food production for numerous basic commodities. At the same time, however, farmers and national economics are already being damaged by the problems of food surplus on an international scale. Agricultural research, playing center stage in this world food situation, has become both a miracle worker and villain in the eyes of many.

This relatively short book addresses both the major problems and major issues of agricultural research and its public policy implications. The editors explain current conditions in the introductory chapter. We want to point out primarily that agricultural research produces both political winners and losers and, as a consequence, supporters and critics. Chapter 2, by Alan I. Marcus, traces the development of American public research institutions in terms of support from winners and the benefits winners derived. This analysis is particularly important because the model for international agricultural development comes directly from these research institutions. In short, US winners have often been duplicated worldwide, a factor that many find objectionable in a world of pluralistic food needs.

Part II of the book turns to contemporary problems and alternative agricultural approaches. C. Ford Runge, in Chapter 3, lays out the need for considering alternatives. He notes that recent financial problems in agriculture result from investments in high-technology, capital-intensive farming. Correctives cannot be applied by current economic/agricultural policy instruments, and the results are liable to force many of the best educated and most technically proficient farmers out of business. Will the implications be manageable for American agriculture in its present condition?

With that question of sustainability in mind, Garth Youngberg turns to an analysis of alternatives in Chapter 4. Without retreating to such restrictive practices as organic farming, because such a position would surely doom alternative agriculture, Youngberg argues for balance. Specifically, he wants policy-makers to look at the basic implications of biological research on a widespread basis, much like Runge did on behalf of one variable, the producer.

Is it likely that policy-makers will respond? The next two chapters, in Part III, suggest that they might give serious consideration to issues currently under debate. Chapter 5 by Hemchandra Gajbhiye and Don Hadwiger examines the present basis of political support for high technology research. Their focus is both national and international. Challenges are forthcoming, they predict, if the food benefits are not clearly articulated as worthwhile in terms of obvious social costs. In Chapter 6, Bill Browne examines these criticisms more specifically in terms of American agricultural policy results. He finds complaints growing in number and importance but, as yet, lacking a committed constituency for change.

The final part of the book, in light of these criticisms and policy complaints, turns to the prospects for policy change. J. Patrick Madden, in Chapter 7, challenges the agricultural academy from economists to agronomists to address the implications of their work. They are the ones best equipped to do so and most in place for a self-policing review. Few others, our other authors suggest, have either the insights or economic interests to undertake this review.

Chapter 8, by Frederick H. Buttel and Martin Kenney, looks at facilitating agricultural institutions in developing countries as vehicles for making biotechnological breakthroughs work where the green revolution failed earlier. To accomplish meaningful change in those countries, their governments will actively have to deliver technology and ensure its proper use. Without the same diligence and resolve called for earlier by Madden, there will be more failures than successes in resolving the past and present dilemmas of agricultural research.

We feel that our authors have brought together eight suggestive and insightful papers. Their comments and findings should be studied carefully by those who have either unrestrained enthusiasm for or great suspicions of the future directions of agricultural research. To concentrate on the negative and forget the historical benefits of research would be a mistake of disastrous proportions. To ignore the agricultural research establishment in its time of greatest controversy and adversity would be a disservice for all who have and will continue to benefit from its very real contributions. Nor do we want to ignore its fallacies, however. This is the conclusion of all of us and the central reason why we participated in this project.

In addition to thanking our authors, Hadwiger and Browne wish to acknowledge a few others. Kenneth R. Farrell, Director of the National Center for Food and Agricultural Policy of Resources for the Future, supported this project financially and with counsel. So too did the Economic Research Service of the United States Department of Agriculture, the Iowa Agricultural Experiment Station, and the Farm Foundation. We owe much to their ongoing institutional concern for agricultural policy.

DON F. HADWIGER
WILLIAM P. BROWNE

Notes on the Contributors

William P. Browne is Professor of Political Science, Central Michigan University.

Frederick H. Buttel is Professor of Sociology, Cornell University.

Hemchandra Gajbhiye is a graduate student at Iowa State University.

Don F. Hadwiger is Professor of Political Science, Iowa State University.

Martin Kenney is Assistant Professor of Sociology, Ohio State University.

J. Patrick Madden is Professor of Sociology, Pennsylvania State University.

Alan I. Marcus is Associate Professor of History, Iowa State University.

Carlisle Ford Runge is Associate Professor of Economics, University of Minnesota.

I. Garth Youngberg is Director, Institute for Alternative Agriculture.

Part I

Agricultural Research in a Policy Setting

1 Introduction

Don F. Hadwiger and William P. Browne

Public agricultural research has made an enormous and timely contribution to world peace, justice and well-being by enabling the agricultural sectors to produce more food at moderate prices. We are witnessing market abundance, in the midst of a world 'population explosion' which was once expected to hasten doomsday. Populous nations such as India and China have become virtually self-sufficient in food production, as have Western Europe and other areas previously characterized as food-deficient. In many such countries the challenge to produce more must now coexist with the new challenge to increase the effective demand for food.

Agricultural research, having contributed so much, promises more. There is widespread optimism in the scientific community that we are at a point of breakthroughs in biotechnology from which, in coming decades, greater abundance and efficiency will flow.

Despite their contribution and the prospect of greater contributions, public agricultural research institutions are suffering adversity. In the United States, the national agricultural research agencies have suffered personnel cuts. Resources are declining also within the state institutions – the colleges of agriculture and their experiment stations. In some developing countries agricultural research institutions are coming of age, but in others they are regularly victimized by unstable politics. A new set of international research centers is experiencing tight funding. Private agricultural research, previously devoted mainly to brand-name product development, has gained venture capital for pursuing technology breakthroughs, but private research on the whole has suffered along with other sectors from the effects of the US agricultural recession.

US and international research institutions are not being allowed to grow, and indeed some budgets are inadequate for system maintenance. Certainly, funding is far below levels that are justified based on returns to investment. Adversity despite achievement is a paradox for which several explanations are offered here:

1. The agricultural sector which supports applied research has suffered a loss of representation and strategic power positions.
2. Research funding is politically controversial because many

interested groups are more inclined to complain about what they do not like than to offer firm support for the research that they want.
3. Research politics is moving from a distributive 'pork barrel' process to a redistributive budget recission process.
4. Agricultural research is relatively unsheltered in the budget process, and indeed becomes even more vulnerable as a result of budget cuts. If agencies cannot replenish themselves, they may become less worthy for funding, and lose their political stamina.
5. The current agricultural depression has depleted the class of innovative farmers who were the principal users of public research, and has damaged other parts of the technology infrastructure.

Despite suffering these adversities, research institutions are gaining a new basis for political acceptance or 'legitimacy'. Through the development of a worldwide network, these institutions have demonstrated that the benefits of agricultural technology can be widely shared, even in developing countries. Infrastructure requirements which some poor countries found it difficult to meet are less inhibiting under emerging biotechnology. Public research institutions are also moving impressively to find agricultural technologies that do not cause environmental deterioration as an unwanted side-effect – technologies which are therefore sustainable as well as efficient.

By providing more abundant and inexpensive food for the world's numerous consumers, by extending this technology into developing nations, and by working toward an environmentally sustainable technology, the public agricultural research system has enhanced its 'political legitimacy' – that is, its acceptance by political actors as a useful and appropriate function of government. Having gained political legitimacy, research institutions should now seek more support on the national and international level.

At the same time research institutions continue to receive major support from the 'first users' of research – innovative farmers and other agribusiness. It is suggested here that the class of innovative, enlarging farmers may be declining, but there may be new sets of research users including 'alternative agriculturalists' and multinational biotechnology firms.

So while public research institutions have gained new opportunities based on their technology achievements, they must continue to accept the burden of political self-advocacy, recognizing that major beneficiaries are still not effectively organized as supporters. As yet, greater progress has been made in distributing benefits from research than in allocating support for it.

TIME OF ADVERSITY

One hears the argument that the agricultural system has overachieved, and therefore 'society' – an overarching decision-maker – is quite rationally putting on the brakes. But that easy explanation is fallacious both as to facts and dynamics.

With respect to facts, it is not true that the world in general has too much food. Measured in terms of physiological need, the problem is not overproduction but underdistribution. Some developing nations still confront a growing population–food imbalance. In Chapter 8 Fred Buttel discusses strategies by which such nations might use new biotechnology to meet their enormous food needs. Also, there are indications that our current high-productivity system needs some redirection to preserve our soil and our natural environment, as Garth Youngberg and Patrick Madden discuss in Chapters 4 and 7 respectively.

With respect to dynamics, Alan Marcus explains in Chapter 2 that the support for agricultural research within the US has not come from 'society' but from a complex interaction between farmer groups and scientist groups.

Declining support from the agricultural sector

During a century and a half of public agricultural research in the United States, as Marcus points out, there were two principal political actors – farmers and agricultural scientists. Each sought dominance, and therefore each constituted a pole structuring this relationship. At one pole were the farmers. At first farmers intended to do their own research, and they did before 1870. Farmer research emphasized improved machines in order to make easier the way of life which they preferred. The land grant colleges, chartered in 1862, were not intended to be mainly research agencies but rather institutions of enlightenment to enrich the rural way of life. As research agencies the colleges were at first considered failures.

At the other pole were scientists, united in thinking that they should determine the direction of research, and that the farmers' role should be to listen to and adopt their findings. A blended relationship evolved. Farmers controlled the first state experiment stations. But when the experiment stations were chartered nationally in the Hatch Act, they were placed on college campuses. Meanwhile, scientists working within the US Department of Agriculture (USDA) won a major place for science within that agency, and each catastrophe in agriculture over the years has provided another boost for US research governed by scientists. Congress became the political sponsor of federal research.

At the state level, establishment of the extension services after 1914 freed the state experiment station scientists from direct contact with farmers. The colleges themselves formed national associations to support research. Scientists strengthened their immediate control over research institutions by insisting that they should be headed by scientists.

Meanwhile, farmers through their organizations, and researchers through their organizations, reached agreement on the goal of agricultural research: improved efficiency. It was convenient for both parties to decentralize research – to relate it to particular commodities, regions and problems. Thus, there was no one farm problem to which research was devoted, but rather many farm problems. Agricultural research solved problems and created income opportunities for specific sets of producers. Research leaders successfully traded on the support of these various producers. Yet agricultural scientists also pursued a utopian vision of a rural society in which there was leisure and abundant food production, achieved through improved agricultural technology. Agricultural scientists promoted research both for its usefulness to sets of producers and its utopian achievements. Both arguments mobilized rural legislators in the US, who until a decade ago were quite numerous, and who also held strategic power positions.

Changes in group structure

Today rural interests are a minority. Furthermore, as William Brown points out, they are neither enthusiastic nor wholehearted supporters of public research. The general farm organizations give perfunctory support at congressional hearings. Specific recommendations come from one general organization, the American Farm Bureau Federation, and from groups representing particular commodities. For all agricultural groups, however, research is not the main policy concern.

The truly vigorous supporters of agricultural research are the research organizations themselves: for example, the land grant colleges, the Agricultural Research Institute, and the American Veterinary Medical Association. As in the past, the burden of political advocacy falls mainly on scientist leaders.

Meanwhile, many groups voice complaints. The following are categories of complaints, and those who make them:

1. Research benefits are sluiced to those producers seeking research and to the researchers themselves, rather than to farmers generally. This complaint arises from public interest groups who want benefits for small farmers, consumers, and others.
2. Products developed by researchers are not always safe and nutritious, say consumer groups.
3. Food industry groups complain that the products are not always developed to be most attractive to consumers.
4. Modern agriculture adversely affects the natural environment, say environmental groups. Economic development agencies add that agricultural pollution also impedes the development of recreation and tourism in states in which those industries are competitive with agriculture.
5. Private agricultural researchers complain that public findings are released into the public domain, providing unfair competition with those who seek to profit from knowledge.

These critics are not likely to form an alliance against research institutions because their individual interests collectively lack consonance, but these various criticisms make research programs 'controversial' and therefore vulnerable to the budget cutters' ax. A more logical response to these complaints may be to add research projects directed to them. The political environment offers problems to be solved but does not easily grant the resources to solve them.

From a distributive to a redistributive policy environment

Formerly the coalition of farmers and scientists operated in a milieu of distributive policy. A few well-placed decision-makers, such as members of the appropriations committees, were continually chartering new agricultural research projects. Indeed, such projects became 'pork barrel' items which rural legislators proudly returned to their districts.

That environment has changed. With shrinking public resources, distributive politics is no longer so fruitful. In recent years, for example, legislators have continued to add new research laboratories and projects but without adequate increases in total funding to sustain the existing functions. Agency budgets are decided within a milieu of redistributive politics, in which one party must lose in order for another to gain. In this redistributive milieu, public research institutions are disadvantaged in several ways. First, major budget decisions which cut the pie in large slices may overlook the merits of relatively small budgets such as that of agricultural research. Second, when a choice must be made between short-term palliatives and long-term remedies, decision-makers are usually under pressure to save those programs which are producing immediate benefits. Third, since many programs are protected from budget cuts – for example, entitlement and lending programs – others including research suffer the brunt of the budget ax. In the Gramm–Rudman–Hollings measure implementing a balanced US budget, for example, some major programs are exempted from across-the-board cuts, but not public research.

Cuts which reduce the vitality of agencies have secondary impacts. Agencies which are denied adequate facilities for maintenance and growth may become less innovative, less worthy of support, less aggressive in advocating for themselves, and ultimately less respected as political participants.

Changes in the infrastructure of agriculture

Public agricultural research may also be losing some of its primary clientèle of innovative farmers. Economist Ford Runge suggests that current financial trends may disadvantage the young, well-educated, technologically advanced farmers who assumed large debt loads in the 1970s and early 1980s. Since many of these farmers have remained 'efficient' from a technological perspective, their displacement has been due to financial conditions rather than crop-growing performance.

Ford Runge provides evidence that technology, per se, is less important than financial forces in explaining structural change in agriculture. In the past, farm size increased because the opportunity cost of machinery was less than that of labor. This relationship reversed between 1970 and 1976: labor became cheaper than machinery. With this reversal, farm size increases decelerated, although financial advantages continued to benefit larger farmers. However, those who took on too much credit in the expectation of ever-rising exports and land values, abetted by lenders as well as many economists, are now the most seriously in trouble. The cause remains financial, rather than technological. Indeed, burdensome debt is borne disproportionately by enlarged farmers many of whom remain technologically efficient. One Minnesota survey found that over half of the big farms had debt–asset ratios above the currently 'safe' level of 40 per cent; as the value of land and machinery assets continues to drop, the position of these indebted farms becomes even more tenuous.

RESPONSE TO ADVERSITY

To survive and grow under adverse conditions, agricultural research institutions are seeking to strengthen support from two basic constituencies: from the immediate users of new technology – the farmers and agribusinesses – with whom the scientists have a longstanding relationship; and from utopian or public interest elites who appreciate the enormous impact of new agricultural technology. The latter particularly include those who wish to reduce world hunger, those who want to prevent environmental pollution, and those who wish to preserve social institutions such as family agriculture. Suggestions are made for improving support from both constituencies.

Moving from monocultural, high-input agriculture

Agricultural research has been effective partly because researchers have addressed real problems using multi-disciplinary approaches. Both Garth Youngberg and Patrick Madden counsel scientists to resist the disciplinary pathologies which draw researchers away from problems and clients. Indeed, Youngberg encourages an even broader focus, a systems approach to agricultural production. Youngberg, Director of the Institute for Alternative Agriculture, has suggested that low-input agricultural systems may be the more sustainable in this age of agricultural abundance and environmental pollution.

Youngberg explains that over the last forty years the trend to large-scale, highly specialized capital- and energy-intensive farms has resulted in a very large growth in per acre output. Problems have resulted, including the erosion and chemical pollution of soil and water, adverse environments for humans, and foods laced with chemicals, as well as problems with declining potency of chemicals.

As a result of these problems, Youngberg thinks, there is increased interest in low-input agriculture, both among scientists and producers. Evidence of this includes the heavy demand for a US Department of Agriculture report on organic farming, and a report on the recent investigations into organic farming by the National Research Council's Board of Agriculture.

Prospective changes may make low-input agriculture more viable.

These changes include the possible repeal of federal tax and credit policies which encouraged capital-intensive farming, new consumer attitudes favoring chemical-free food, and emerging environmental measures which, for example, tax fertilizers and pesticides as a means of paying for environmental damages. In addition, reduced demand for food exports, as other nations produce their own food, may mean reduced incentives for high-input technologies. Possibly the breakthroughs in biotechnology research will reduce dependence on agricultural chemicals, although, as Youngberg notes, one of the first commercial results of the breakthrough in biotechnology has been to rejuvenate a major herbicide for use on soybean acreage.

Preventing social and ecological damage

There have been undesired side-effects from modern agricultural technology, such as the chemical pollution that now impairs water used for human consumption. But new technology can also provide remedies for such technology side-effects. For example, minimum tillage may reduce soil erosion. Integrated pest management, a systematic approach, may reduce dependence on chemicals.

At one time the only criterion for selecting research projects was whether they promoted efficiency. This was based on faulty assumptions: that increased abundance in itself always benefits all, that any costly side-effects from the technology would have been anticipated, and that 'society' would have decided whether costs outweigh benefits. Instead, Madden points out, side-effects often occur after the technology has been used. Madden suggests that the research institutions should adopt a 'new covenant', committing themselves to be 'scientifically excellent, socially relevant, and ecologically responsible'. Indeed, new legislative mandates and governing mechanisms are moving agencies toward such a commitment. Agricultural research agencies will certainly gain wide acceptance ('legitimacy') as they demonstrate their determination to avoid unwanted side-effects, and as they persuade others that these side-effects are best remedied by improving technology rather than by retreating from modern agriculture.

It is a large task to create a responsible technology, and that should be good news for a research establishment which is looking for a continuing role.

Distributing research benefits to developing nations

Another large task, increasingly facilitated by improved technology, is to improve the distribution of food. Reduced cost of production has made food more accessible to poor people. The development and adaptation of high-yielding crops has produced the 'green revolution' within developing countries, with mixed but on balance enormously beneficent results.

International research centers

Populous developing countries such as India and China are becoming self-sufficient in basic foods, and in this achievement both technology and organization have played a part. As Hemchandra Gajbhiye and Don Hadwiger point out, agricultural scientists have led the development of an international research system that links a set of international research centers with public research agencies in the developed and the developing countries.

Significant international support for the international centers began in 1972 with establishment of the International Rice Research Institute (IRRI) in the Philippines. Support is channeled through the Consultative Group on International Agricultural Research (CGIAR), whose donor members include national governments, multinational agencies, banks and foundations. These centers have encouraged the development of national research agencies within developing countries, and have worked with national agencies, for example in the adaptation of new varieties of seeds. Universities in developed countries, over a long span of years, have assisted in developing professional capacity within developing country research institutions. Some developing country institutions have gained the capacity to disseminate technology, but as Vernon Ruttan (1982) has pointed out, such institutional development requires much time, and with unstable politics there are many setbacks.

A proposal for public research corporations

Fred Buttel and Martin Kenney suggest that breakthroughs in biotechnology may permit the development of other delivery mechanisms. Buttel and Kenney believe that the new biotechnology offers great potential for nations whose agriculture is still poorly developed. However, much biotechnology research is now in the private sector, and Buttel and Kenney are fearful that private companies might deny its benefits to those who cannot afford to buy it.

According to these authors, the biotechnology industry includes two kinds of private research actors: first, the startup companies – small firms, located mostly in the US, that are doing innovative theoretical and practical research; second, large chemical, pharmaceutical and oil companies that are multinational in scope. The multinational companies are becoming involved by investing in startup companies, by letting research contracts to startup companies, and also by forming relationships with universities.

The less developed countries are, or should be, greatly interested in the emerging biotechnology, say Buttel and Kenney, because the new information may be adaptable even without a large infrastructure, and with a small cadre of educated personnel. Indeed, Buttel thinks developing countries can benefit more from this revolution than from the earlier 'green revolution', because the biotechnology revolution has application beyond the basic food grains.

Proprietary considerations will be important. The big industrial input companies will seek to control technology through gaining patents, as in their current move to purchase seed companies. Second, these companies are market-orientated, so although they will find large markets in some developing countries, they may ignore the areas that cannot pay. Those who do receive information from the corporations might become dependent on them.

Kenney and Buttel suggest that the governments of developing countries could form public corporations as vehicles to deliver this technology. Such corporations could also nurture infant industries which are using the technology. But they note, realistically, that developing-country governments are reluctant to engage in long-term planning such as would be required here, and there would be opposition within some governments which are already under the influence of multinational corporations.

New co-operation in technology distribution

Apparently there remains a large role for public research institutions in nurturing an international scientific community, and in further developing a set of institutions which can produce and distribute technology. Leaders of these institutions must also generate political support for agricultural research.

Experience indicates that support must be generated at two levels. At one level are the organizations representing first users of research

– traditionally the farm groups with whom the scientists formed a complex interaction. First users throughout the world are still important supporters of research, and the system must be adequately decentralized to respond to their demands.

At another level are the public interest groups, eleemosynary foundations, and governments which want a technology that is highly productive but also environmentally sustainable, and which is also equitable in the distribution of its benefits.

The public agricultural research system is in a better position than ever to meet all those demands, and emerging technology offers the prospect that future investments in agricultural research will be even more rewarding. In a timely response to escalating food needs, new technology has been created and disseminated despite the lack of infrastructure in some areas. It is equally imperative to develop a sustainable technology which does not pollute the environment or have other unwanted side-effects.

It can be seen that public agricultural research institutions, while suffering adversity, also have abundant opportunities. Their recent achievements have made them more 'legitimate', or worthy of public support. Indeed, as Vernon Ruttan has noted, national and international developmental agencies now perceive that agricultural research has a very high pay-off by comparison with some other expenditures. There is also symbolic value in assisting nations to develop their agriculture, as indicated at the 1974 World Food Conference.

Technology and its dissemination are clearly international activities, even though they are usually supported by first users. It would seem that there is opportunity for greater multinational effort, and good reason for rather diverse nations to join in support of it. Indeed, fairness requires that all nations which can afford to do so should share in the support of agricultural research and training. Perhaps international treaties should provide a new entitlement for public agricultural research budgets. Leadership in organizing support must come, as it always has, largely from the agricultural science community.

Reference

Ruttan, V. W. (1982) *Agricultural Research Policy* (Minneapolis: University of Minnesota Press).

2 Constituents and Constituencies: An Overview of the History of Public Agricultural Research Institutions in America

Alan I. Marcus

The nature of American agricultural research has been the subject of an intense debate during the past several decades. Land-grant colleges, agricultural experiment stations, and the United States Department of Agriculture have drawn public ire (Hightower, 1973; Berry, 1977; Friedland and Kappel, 1979; Vogeler, 1981). They also have generated a vigorous defense (McCalla, 1978; Ruttan, 1982; Busch and Lacy, 1983, pp. 167–204). Two questions rest at the heart of the matter. Is publicly funded agricultural research to assist small farmers, agribusiness, and/or consumers, and does it accomplish its mission(s) well? The first query raises a host of political and ethical issues – the fate of rural communities, the role of minorities in agriculture and agricultural research, justification for continued public funding, and the like. The second depends to a great degree on the answer to the first. But it also hinges on the measurement of effectiveness: is effectiveness measured by cost, immediate applications, long-range goals, or in some other way?

The agitation engendered by these concerns suggests a lack of consensus about agricultural research. The absence of agreement on its aims and adequacy is not bad *per se*, of course, and public scrutiny may well be the initial step in formulating a broad based consensus. More to the point, however, is that the lack of consensus about agricultural research is not a recent phenomenom. At least since the 1870s, Americans have disputed publicly supported agricultural research's form and function. Those disputes helped shape those institutions, their methods and their agendas, many of which continue in force today; the current network of public agricultural research in the United States is in part a product of those earlier arguments. Those debates have not always been decided in the same manner. Nor have they covered the same ground. Agricultural research in America has changed goals and approaches. Nonetheless, an investigation of these debates can prove informative. It can provide the context from which to view the current situation as well as a sense of the complexity of the problems. Both may be crucial in formulating contemporary policy.

Prior to the 1870s, American farmers did virtually all their own research. Much of this activity was public and publicly funded. Agricultural newspapers and agricultural societies, many of which received state monies, were the media through which farmers engaged in these research efforts. Working farmers also adjudicated the success of the research. Field trials at state fairs and plantings on society-owned plots – there were over 900 agricultural societies on the eve of the Civil War – provided graphic evidence of the efficacy of particular methods. Agriculturists also had free reign to set research agendas. Their societies offered premiums, prizes and bounties to stimulate research aimed at solving particular problems (Hurt, 1982; Rossiter, 1976; Knoblauch *et al.*, 1962, pp. 2–3).

Agricultural research ran along certain lines during this period. Farmers emphasized mechanical contrivances, not chemical or biological processes. And they suited their efforts to the immediate problems at hand. Their research generally was aimed at developing a way or at least an easier way to undertake some seemingly impossible or particularly onerous task. The development of a plow to break the plains, to make farming possible there, might be a good example. Engaging in agricultural research sparingly and on a circumscribed scope, farmers did not seek to re-orient or reconstitute agriculture. Instead, they sought to make it possible to farm, to eke out an existence and still have time to participate in familial and social life. To put one's hands in the soil, to be in tune with nature, was the key (Ward, 1955). Farming itself was a way of life and its practice the ultimate reward.

That is not to romanticize farming. Rather, it is to indicate that its practitioners' ambitions manifested themselves in institutional forms. The agitation for agricultural and mechanical colleges in the 1840s and 1850s and the passage of the Morrill Land-Grant Act in 1862 were not inspired by a notion that agricultural practice and life needed dramatic correction or improvement. Instead, the movement and the

Act primarily served to provide farmers' and laborers' children with opportunities similar to those of their more wealthy contemporaries: they too could receive a broad, not vocationally based, education. Their minds fortified, these children would presumably return to farms and factories, as well as any other occupation they might choose. The result was to be a better America, one in which its yeomen possessed the benefits available to their more well-to-do brothers (US Congress, 1862; Ross, 1938; Wiser, 1962; Peffer, 1966; Marti, 1971).

Neither the formation of the United States Department of Agriculture, also in 1862, nor the soil analysis craze of the early 1850s reflected a challenge to the basic assumption that farming was a way of life. The creation of the USDA merely signified that agriculture remained important to the national health; it recognized agriculture, nothing more. Indeed, the Act did not establish a working department in any conventional sense. It only allowed for the appointment of a commissioner of agriculture and a statistician to record agricultural progress. The USDA was to serve as a central repository, a museum. It was to collect all information concerning agriculture and to store plants and seeds. Indeed, the commissioner was not even granted the power or money to hire a staff; he had precious few duties (US Congress, 1862a; True, 1937). The soil analysis craze was a brief flirtation with the idea that chemistry could enable farmers to determine whether agriculture was possible; a simple test could predict if crops would grow on a plot or if intervention in the form of fertilizer was required. It passed from public view rather swiftly (Gates, 1962; Rossiter, 1975).

Satisfaction with the USDA, agricultural colleges, agriculture, and the pursuit of agricultural research began to wane around 1870. It was replaced during the decade with an intensity of feeling that bordered on hostility. Farmers constantly complained that American agricultural practice and life was outmoded and that the USDA and the colleges had not come to their aid. They questioned the wisdom of forming these institutions and maintained that the schools and the USDA had become sinecures. In effect, they argued that agriculture lagged behind other late nineteenth-century occupations and suffered further because it received little assistance from government (Nevins, 1962; Scott, 1972; Nordin, 1974).

The farmers' critique was unlike any earlier assessment, and not because of its sharp tone. It indicated a change in desires, a change in what farmers expected to receive from agriculture. Agriculture now seemed an occupation, less a way of life. It had become a type of expertise in which success was measured by production and the ability to produce. Its practitioners sought to increase production and lower their costs. They wanted to rationalize operations and to conduct their affairs efficiently so as to reap the greatest profit. That seemed an end in itself. Indeed, the actual practice of farming had become onerous, its primary reward was money to enjoy the material fruits of late nineteenth-century American life (Persons, 1973).

The desire to secure as large a profit as possible accentuated production. It placed a premium on techniques and processes that would enable farmers to slash their overheads while stepping up their output. That sparked considerable interest in implementing new, cheaper farm methods as well as searching for even newer, less expensive techniques. In effect, emphasis on agricultural production led to a corresponding emphasis on agricultural research.

That the pace of agricultural research would heighten remained without question. What that meant and who would attempt it was the subject of much debate. Many farmers called for agricultural societies to redouble their research efforts, while others urged their brethren to announce new discoveries in agricultural periodicals. They expected societies and newspapers to announce rules developed by farmers that would systematize operations and procedures on the farm and maximize productivity and production. And they deprecated agricultural colleges for not pursuing the same agenda. To most farmers, colleges were failed institutions. Their staffs had not provided results or given any inkling that they were engaged in the search (Marcus, 1985, pp. 32–42).

These attacks on agricultural colleges were unprecedented and unfair. The schools had not been established for those tasks. In any case, they were not research institutions in any sense. Nevertheless, many of their faculties sympathized with the farmers' laments. They too sought to increase agricultural production but they deemed farm systematization inappropriate and ineffective. These academicians maintained that farmers themselves lacked the expertise to improve yields. Agricultural college personnel claimed that only they could solve the farm problem, that only they possessed the expertise necessary to make two blades of grass grow where one had before. They based their assessment on their special training, knowledge and method; they called themselves agricultural scientists. This expertise would enable them to determine and verify the laws of plant and animal growth. They recognized the farmers' job as learning of their revelations at agricultural colleges, farmers' institutes and short courses, and applying these techniques to the soil (Marcus, 1986).

The agricultural scientists' program was new. Indeed, they were a new group. Few in the 1860s or before in America claimed agricultural science as an expertise; to a large degree, the expertise of agricultural college men was self-proclaimed, a product of the cultural shift from character to expertise, the same shift that transformed agriculture from a way of life – a character-building exercise – to an occupation – a form of expertise. The scientists' assertions also set out a new notion of what agricultural colleges were to do. These schools were to teach the principles of successful farming, the scientific laws on which modern farming was based. They were to become in that sense vocational schools and not just for students enrolled full-time. They were to serve the agricultural public, a constituency different from before. And they were to serve this constituency in a specific way, which would diminish its members. Farmers had long held that they were capable of understanding farming processes, developing new techniques, and applying them. Agricultural scientists argued that farmers could only apply knowledge, not produce it. The job of agricultural scientists was to preach and that of farmers was to practice what agricultural scientists preached (Marcus, 1986).

Although agricultural scientists stood united on these points, they achieved no similar consensus on what constituted agricultural science, where it ought to be pursued, and what techniques to employ. They repeatedly disputed these issues among themselves. Some argued that all agricultural processes were reducible to chemical equations, while others measured climatic factors, investigated breeding, experimented in soil physics, and attempted to gauge the parameters of plant and animal health. Many maintained that only in laboratories could scientists verify results and control variables. Others opted for field experiments because that site replicated actual farming practices. They suggested that numerous repetitions of a single experiment at different loci would prove an adequate substitute for absolute certainty. In no instance was there an agreed set of procedures and techniques to examine any single agricultural phenomenon; each scientist carried on in the manner he saw fit (Marcus, 1985, pp. 59–64).

These college scientists lacked the agreements that would lead in a few short years to the creation of disciplines (Rossiter, 1979). Farmers had no such worries. Almost to a man, agriculturists opposed the agricultural scientists' program as impractical, not germane to farming. Only in one circumstance did farmers find a use for scientists, and then not because of their scientific attainments but for their potential technical capabilities. They wanted chemists to certify that artificial manures contained the ingredients for which they paid; farmers were concerned about fertilizer frauds and demanded that state governments employ chemists to analyze fertilizer components.

Many states east of the Mississippi complied and in the 1870s established offices of state chemist. Connecticut seemingly went further. It formed an agricultural experiment station in 1875. This institution's name conjured up images of German stations, which engaged in agricultural research. The Connecticut station did not. Despite its designation, the Connecticut station dealt almost exclusively with fertilizer analyses; it was a state chemistry shop. And the stations erected in North Carolina in 1877 and New Jersey in 1880 were of a similar ilk. All were organizationally separate from agricultural colleges, operated under farmer-dominated boards of control, and did little aside from fertilizer analyses. It remained until 1882 for a station to be created on different premises. It, too, had to please farmers.

The New York station was the entity that broke with tradition. It was America's first publicly funded agricultural science research institute. It explicitly took the increase of farmers' profits as its aim and the methods of science as its means. It systematically attempted both to derive the rules of farm operations and the laws of agricultural science. It pursued investigations in the laboratory and the field. It employed a diverse staff, each of whom possessed scientific credentials. The New York station stood as a compromise between the objectives of farmers and scientists. Agricultural colleges were not included. Like earlier stations, the New York station was responsible to a board of control composed primarily of farmers. While the station's director set its agenda, his tenure in that office depended upon the board's approval (Marcus, 1986a).

Passage of the Hatch Agricultural Experiment Station Act in 1887 institutionalized a version of that compromise nationwide. The Act provided each state and territory $15 000 annually to fund an experiment station devoted exclusively to agricultural experimentation and investigation. The Hatch Act was faithful in its conception to the New York station, except in one important way. It recognized agricultural colleges as legitimate sites for agricultural research (US Congress, 1887). That victory was a tribute to the colleges themselves. Unable to secure an agricultural research role on the state level, they had carried their crusade to Congress as early as 1882. There they found the farmers' political clout somewhat diluted. Through a series of adroit maneuvers, agricultural schools managed to place farmers in the position of accepting the Hatch Act or receiving nothing. That many farmers ultimately backed the Act despite their animus towards colleges testified to their desperation (Marcus, 1985, pp. 188–211).

A similar contentiousness between farmers and agricultural scientists dominated the debates over the USDA's future. Farmers struck first. They demanded little from the agency itself. Instead, they focused on raising the commissioner to cabinet rank. A Secretary of Agriculture in the cabinet would advise the President about farmers' concerns, a move that would not only provide agriculture with more political leverage but also signify that it remained the nation's foremost industry (National Grange, 1879). Agricultural scientists had grander plans. Prior to the Hatch Act's passage, they hoped to convert the USDA into the nation's chief agricultural science investigative agency and argued that its staff be comprised entirely of pre-eminent scientists (American Agricultural Association, 1881). The enthusiasm of agricultural college scientists for this proposal cooled in 1887. The Hatch Act created numerous agricultural science research institutes, and the formation of a single, first-rank national agency threatened to end their autonomy.

Those scientists already at work in the USDA (and their number increased dramatically with every agricultural cataclysm – plagues of grasshoppers, outbreaks of hog cholera, and the like) persisted in the push for the USDA to become the country's leading agricultural research institution. They were generally successful, but the results were gradual. Departments and bureaus were added almost continually from the 1880s (Ross, 1946; True, 1937). Agricultural college scientists also gained. When Congress established the Office of Experiment Stations within the USDA in 1888, it limited the Office's duties to advising stations and serving as a medium of communications. It did not grant the Office the authority to direct station research activities; that remained the prerogative of each station (Atwater, 1889 and 1889a). Farmers also won their point. In 1889, Congress elevated agriculture to the cabinet (True, 1937, pp. 172–7).

The new USDA initiatives and the enactment of the Hatch Act established a *de facto* national system of agricultural research. It tended to remove agricultural research from state farmers and to conceive of farmers as a single national group. State legislatures and state concerns seemed less immediate. Congress began to predominate.

These trends were elaborated during the next three decades. One manifestation of the system's national character was its dependence on national legislation and the USDA's rising influence. The Second Morrill Act (1890) and the Adams Act (1906) appropriated additional federal monies for agricultural colleges and stations. The Smith-Lever Act (1914) created a network of federally supported county extension agents, who worked to bring farmers the fruits of agricultural research (Rosenberg, 1976; Rainsford, 1972; Scott, 1972, pp. 151ff). At the same time, the agents freed college scientists from their public; scientists no longer had to respond to farmers' inquiries. But perhaps the most important indication of the national locus of agricultural research was the USDA's sponsorship and funding of independent researchers. It originated in the 1890s the practice of granting monies to scientists to pursue investigative lines that lay outside the agency's normal endeavors. In effect, it began to set its own research agenda (Baker *et al.*, 1963).

The USDA and Congress did not operate alone on the national level. Colleges, their scientists, and farmers also adopted that locus. Each attempted to establish its own niche within the national system. The American Association of Agricultural Colleges and Experiment Stations (AAAC & ES) was formed in 1887 explicitly to co-ordinate nationwide college and station labors. It attracted college administrators (Myrick, 1887). The emergence of scientific disciplines and the corresponding creation of national disciplinary organizations complicated matters. Each marked out its own turf, established its own methodology, and acted according to its own paradigms (Rossiter, 1979). Farmers' organizations also sought a piece of the pie. The Farmers' Alliance, National Grange, and the local and state farm bureaus lobbied Congress, the USDA, and the AAAC & ES so that agricultural research would meet farmers' concerns (Kile, 1921; Atkeson, 1916).

This research system had arisen from a notion of the desirability of increased agricultural efficiency. Productivity would help farmers. Rationalizing farm operations and activities would put agriculture in line with other late nineteenth- and early twentieth-century American industries and provide farmers with the amenities available to their contemporaries in cities and towns. And while men and women disagreed in several ways about how this objective might best be attained, they nonetheless concurred with its aim (Bowers, 1974;

Danbom, 1979). The creation of the forementioned agricultural research institutions was one of its legacies.

This consensus about basics – not specifics – disintegrated after the First World War. It was replaced by an awareness that increased production was simplistic, at best only part of the answer. The farm situation seemed much more complex. Agricultural research had had and would continue to have consequences, some of which appeared undesirable. This pluralistic thrust in which agriculture and agricultural life seemed alternative occupations and life-styles generated yet another new research agenda. The central question shifted from how to reformulate and change agriculture and agricultural life to attempts to understand, save and cultivate them. Agriculture and agricultural life had become distinct enterprises, unlike any other, and worth tending.

The emergence of agriculture and agricultural life as important occupations and life-styles provided for the entry on a large scale of social scientists into agricultural research. To be sure, some social scientists had been active earlier. They had compared the rural and agricultural with the urban and industrial and noted discrepancies (Shapiro, 1980). In the 1920s and after, however, they produced study after study about the implications of the recent past and its consequences for the present and the future. Two approaches blossomed. Agricultural economists typified the first. Their analyses were predominantly economic, of course, and placed agriculture as an industrial pursuit within the framework of a state, regional, national and world economy. They identified connections and linkages between agricultural practice and the sale of agricultural goods not hinted at earlier, and constructed models to stimulate, build or regain agriculture's profitability (Black, 1929; Ezekiel, 1936; Kirkendall, 1966).

Other social scientists tended to tie the salvation of agriculture more explicitly to the salvation of rural life. These men and women by and large championed the virtues of farm and small-town life. They extolled and measured its coherence, detected those forces working to tear it asunder, elaborated on them and offered programs to restore it to past glory or to prevent its further degeneration (Williams, 1925; Gee, 1930; Terpenning, 1931). Indeed, in a world in which agriculture and rural living seemed styles of work and life, the social scientists' particular expertises became central. That fact did not go unnoticed by the federal government. The Purnell Act (1925), Bankhead-Jones Act (1935) and Agricultural Marketing Act (1946) each provided social scientists with prominent roles in agricultural research and in the agricultural research establishment. Conservation of agriculture and agricultural life assumed a new immediacy (US Congress, 1925, 1935, 1946; Knoblauch *et al.*, 1962, pp. 175–87; Busch and Lacy, 1983: 187).

The new understanding of agriculture as complex and highly integrated manifested itself in new terminology. The nature of these new terms reinforced the apparent utility of social scientists. For example, while earlier researchers had considered markets, products and classes, in the 1920s and thereafter investigators examined marketing, commodities and community. These latter terms had far broader implications: their constituent elements were much more fluid. They reflected not only the post-1920 dynamism accorded agriculture and agricultural life, but also the new perception of interrelatedness between agriculture/rural life and other occupational and life styles. While agriculture and rural life may no longer have seemed the most important styles, they nonetheless remained essential. Put another way, agriculture and rural life may not have appeared crucial or even important in and of themselves. But they were deemed critical because they were perceived as inextricably intertwined with something greater: they were inseparable parts of the supraorganic systems of American, or global, economics and culture.

The post-1920 notion of the complexity of agriculture and rural life also produced important changes in the organization of agricultural research. Both in agricultural experiment stations and the United States Department of Agriculture there was a noticeable blurring of disciplinary lines. The solutions to agricultural problems seemed to rest outside any single specialty's purview. Divisions and disciplines needed to bring their expertises together to bear on particular problems. Agricultural research became problem-oriented and problem-specific. Interdisciplinary research groups, each of which had to be especially constituted to attack a particular problem, became increasingly the manner of organization. In fact, research within the USDA began to be considered an activity – a speciality – separate from other endeavors and with its own staff; researchers themselves seemed to constitute a viable group, different from others no matter what disciplinary or bureau affiliation. This distinction reached its height of formalization in the mid-1950s with the creation of the USDA Agricultural Research Service (Hadwiger, 1982).

This interdisciplinary approach to research found expression in the formation of regional research centers and entities. Indeed, there seemed less a farm problem than farm problems: farmers now appeared divisible by region, farm size, and/or product produced. Farmers as a relatively homogeneous occupation practiced nationwide gave way to a notion of groups of farmers, each of which seemed to have its own difficulties, concerns and agendas. In that sense, for example, corn belt farmers engaged in a pursuit that seemed fundamentally different from that of those of the cotton south. This realization often placed farmers' groups in apparent opposition to one another (Vance, 1929; Black, 1935; Rowe, 1935; Richards, 1936; Nourse *et al.*, 1931; McWilliams, 1935). The new reality was not lost on the USDA. It sent multidisciplinary research teams to work on particular groups' special questions at various sites. Agricultural college specialists usually joined and labored with the USDA staffers there. In some instances, interinstitutional and interdisciplinary co-operation was intentionally short-lived; teams disbanded as soon as they completed their projects (Hartford, 1930; Sweeney and Emley, 1930). But in other cases the efforts proved self-sustaining. The initial research generated new questions which also required answers. The establishment of several agricultural byproduct laboratories in the 1930s was an example of a self-sustaining research venture under USDA auspices (Knight, 1936; Herrick, 1937), while Iowa State College's creation of its Corn Research Institute during the same decade proved a similar initiative under agricultural college control (Buchanan, 1934; Hughes, 1935; Friley, 1938; Ross, 1942).

The notion of interconnectedness also transformed the nature of agricultural research performed by public agencies. The thrust of the pre-1920 efforts had been to isolate factors. In that sense, agricultural research had been essentially structural; it aimed at identifying the components of systems that appeared static. Early animal nutrition work was an apt example. It was a search for the ingredients comprising growth (Armsby, 1890; Smith, 1906; Lusk, 1909). And it reached its pinnacle with the description of vitamin A and B by E. V. McCollum and his Wisconsin station associates in the 1910s (McCollum, 1918). The new research emphasized process, dynamic process. In the social sciences, it translated into examinations of the processes of rural community building and decay or market formation and decline. But the 'hard' sciences also stressed a plan of attack based on the same sort of dynamism. Process reigned supreme. For example, Selman A. Waksman and his New Jersey station team investigated the role of micro-organisms in the dynamic process of soil building and decay. Their studies not only led them to understand humus formation, but also to discover streptomycin and several other antibiotics (Waksman, 1954; Woodruff, 1968). Nor was the thrust of Waksman's work atypical. Jay Lush's animal breeding experiments, Barbara McClintock's transposable corn genetics, Wise Burrough's studies of bovine digestion, and others all reflected the dynamism of the post-1920 period (Lush, 1937; Keller, 1983; Lee, 1984).

The idea of dynamic interrelatedness permeated agricultural research in the years after 1920. It provided agendas for scientists and set research questions. It affected the organization of public research activities and ultimately the pursuit of farming. This notion continues in force today. But an agreement about the importance of interrelatedness did and does not mean that there existed a corresponding agreement on what was interrelated. Quite the opposite was and is the case. It probably cannot be otherwise. The difficulty lay in the notion of interrelatedness itself. It fairly begs for those dissatisfied with the status quo to identify forces as dysfunctional or irrelevant, as antithetical or not germane to their selection of interrelated facets. That is politics, to be sure. It is about personal and group aims, interests and objectives. It is about power. It is not so much a debate about farming or even science or the nation, but rather about who should make policy. It is the science of politics in action.

References

American Agricultural Association (1881) *Journal of the American Agricultural Association*, Vol. 1.

Armsby, Henry P. (1890) *Manual of Cattle-Feeding* (New York: Wiley).

Atkeson, Thomas Clark (1916) *Semi-Centennial History of the Patrons of Husbandry* (New York: Orange Judd).

Atwater, Wilbur O. (1889) 'Report of the Director of the Office of Experiment Stations', *Report of the United States Secretary of Agriculture* (Washington: Government Printing Office), 536–7.

Atwater, Wilbur O. (1889a) 'The What and Why of Agricultural Experiment Stations', *USDA Farmers' Bulletin*, 1: 1–14.

Baker, Gladys L., Wayne D. Rasmussen, Vivian Wiser, and Jane M. Porter (1963) *Century of Service: The First 100 Years of the United States Department of Agriculture* (Washington: Government Printing Office), 36.

Berry, Wendell (1977) *The Unsettling of America: Culture and Agriculture* (Totawa: Sierra Club Books).

Black, John D. (1929) *Agricultural Reform In the United States* (New York: McGraw-Hill).

Black, John D. (1935) *The Dairy Industry and the AAA* (Washington: Brookings Institution).

Bowers, William L. (1974) *The Country Life Movement in America 1900–1920* (Port Washington: Kennikat Press).
Buchanan, R. E. (1934) 'Report on Agricultural Research For the Year Ending June 30, 1934', *Iowa Year Book of Agriculture*, 353–9.
Busch, Lawrence and William B. Lacy (1983) *Science, Agriculture, and the Politics of Research* (Boulder: Westview Press).
Danbom, David B. (1979) *The Resisted Revolution. Urban America and the Industrialization of Agriculture, 1900–1930* (Ames: Iowa State University Press).
Ezekiel, Mordecai (1936) *$2500 A Year: From Scarcity to Abundance* (New York: Harcourt, Brace and World).
Friedland, William H. and Tim Kappel (1979) *Production or Perish: Changing the Inequalities of Agricultural Research Priorities* (Santa Cruz: Project On Social Impact, Assessment and Values).
Friley, Charles E. (1938) *The President's Address to the Staff at the Opening of the Iowa State College Session 1938–39* (Ames: Collegiate Press), 2–3.
Gates, Paul W. (1962) 'The Morrill Act and Early Agricultural Science', *Michigan History*, 46: 289–303.
Gee, Wilson (ed.) (1930) *The Country Life of the Nation* (Chapel Hill: University of North Carolina Press).
Hadwiger, Don F. (1982) *The Politics of Agricultural Research* (Lincoln: University of Nebraska Press), 26–31.
Hartford, C. E. (1930) 'Manufacture and Properties of a Cellulose Product (Maizolith) from Cornstalks and Corncobs', *National Bureau of Standards Miscellaneous Publication #108* (Washington: Government Printing Office).
Herrick, H. T. (1937) 'The Research Program of the Bureau of Chemistry and Soils on Industrial Utilization of Farm Products', *Proceedings of the American Soybean Association*, 3–9.
Hightower, Jim (1973) *Hard Tomatoes, Hard Times* (Cambridge: Schenkman).
Hughes, R. M. (1935) *Address of the President to the Staff of Iowa State College of Agriculture and Mechanic Arts* (Ames: Collegiate Press), 6 and 24–5.
Hurt, R. Douglas (1982) *American Farm Tools: From Hand-Power to Steam-Power* (Manhattan: Sunflower University Press), 4–6.
Keller, Evelyn Fox (1983) *A Feeling For the Organism: The Life and Work of Barbara McClintock* (New York: W. H. Freeman and Co.).
Kile, Orville Merton (1921) *The Farm Bureau Movement* (New York: Macmillan).
Kirkendall, Richard S. (1966) *Social Scientists and Farm Politics In the Age of Roosevelt* (Columbia: University of Missouri Press).
Knight, H. G. (1936) 'Utilization of Farm Wastes', *Condensed Proceedings of the Southern Chemurgic Conference*, 69: 8–14.
Knoblauch, H. C., E. M. Law and W. P. Meyer (1962) *State Agricultural Experiment Stations. A History of Research Policy and Procedure* (Washington: Government Printing Office).
Lee, Harold (1984) *Roswell Garst: A Biography* (Ames: Iowa State University Press), 144–58.

Lush, Jay L. (1937) *Animal Breeding Plans* (Ames: Collegiate Press).
Lusk, Graham (1909) *The Elements of the Science of Nutrition* (Philadelphia: W. B. Saunders).
Marcus, Alan I. (1985) *Agricultural Science and the Quest For Legitimacy. Farmers, Agricultural Colleges and Experiment Stations, 1870–1890* (Ames: Iowa State University Press).
Marcus, Alan I. (1986) 'The Ivory Silo: Farmer-Agricultural College Tensions in the 1870s and 1880s', *Agricultural History*, 60 (January).
Marcus, Alan I. (1986a) 'From State Chemistry to State Science: The Transformation of the Idea of the Agricultural Experiment Station, 1875–1887', in Lawrence Busch and William Lacy (eds) *The Agricultural Scientific Enterprise* (Boulder: Westview Press).
Marti, Donald B. (1971) 'The Purposes of Agricultural Education: Ideas and Projects in New York State, 1819–1865', *Agricultural History*, 45: 271–83.
McCalla, Alex F. (1978) 'Politics of the Agricultural Research Establishment', in Don F. Hadwiger and William P. Browne (eds) *The New Politics of Food* (Lexington: Lexington Books), 77–92.
McCollum, E. V. (1918) *The Newer Knowledge of Nutrition* (New York: MacMillan).
McWilliams, Carey (1935) *Factories In the Field. The Story of Migratory Farm Labor in California* (Boston: Little, Brown).
Myrick, Herbert (1887) 'A New Era In Agriculture', *New England Homestead*, 29 (October): 2–3.
National Grange (1879) *Proceedings*, 40, 94, 124, 127.
Nevins, Allen (1962) *The State Universities and Democracy* (Urbana: University of Illinois Press), 52–68.
Nordin, Dennis S. (1974) *Rich Harvest, A History of the Grange* (Jackson: Mississippi State University Press), 62–3.
Nourse, Edwin G. and Joseph G. Knapp (1931) *The Co-operative Marketing of Livestock* (Washington: Brookings Institution).
Peffer, E. Louise (1966) 'Memorial to Congress on an Agricultural College for California, 1853', *Agricultural History*, 40: 53–6.
Persons, Stow (1973) *The Decline of American Gentility* (New York: Columbia University Press).
Rainsford, George N. (1972) *Congress and Higher Education in the Nineteenth Century* (Knoxville: University of Tennessee Press), 107–14.
Richards, Henry I. (1936) *Cotton and the AAA* (Washington: Brookings Institution).
Rosenberg, Charles E. (1976) *No Other Gods. On Science and Social Thought* (Baltimore: Johns Hopkins University Press), 173–84.
Ross, Earl D. (1938) 'The "Father" of the Land-Grant College', *Agricultural History*, 12: 151–86.
Ross, Earl D. (1942) *A History of the Iowa State College of Agriculture and Mechanic Arts* (Ames: Iowa State College Press), 357.
Ross, Earl D. (1946) 'The United States Department of Agriculture During the Commissionership', *Agricultural History*, 20: 129–43.
Rossiter, Margaret W. (1975) *The Emergence of Agricultural Science. Justus Liebig and the Americans, 1840–1880* (New Haven: Yale University Press), 109–24.

Rossiter, Margaret W. (1976) 'The Organization of Agricultural Improvement in the United States, 1785–1865', in Alexandra Oleson and Sanborn C. Brown (eds) *The Pursuit of Knowledge in the Early American Republic. American Scientific and Learned Societies From Colonial Times to the Civil War* (Baltimore: Johns Hopkins University Press), 280–1.

Rossiter, Margaret W. (1979) 'The Organization of the Agricultural Sciences', in Alexandra Oleson and John Voss (eds) *The Organization of Knowledge in Modern America, 1860–1920* (Baltimore: Johns Hopkins University Press), 211–48.

Rowe, Harold B. (1935) *Tobacco Under the AAA* (Washington: Brookings Institution).

Ruttan, Vernon W. (1982) *Agricultural Research Policy* (Minneapolis: University of Minnesota Press).

Scott, Roy V. (1972) *The Reluctant Farmer. The Rise of Agricultural Extension to 1914* (Urbana: University of Illinois Press).

Shapiro, Henry D. (1980) 'Country Life in the 1880s: The Persisting Past and the Problem of "Two Cultures"', *Hayes Historical Journal*, 3: 51–72.

Smith, Howard R. (1906) *Profitable Stock Feeding* (Lincoln: University of Nebraska Press).

Sweeney, O. R. and W. E. Emley (1930) 'Manufacture of Insulating Board From Corn-Stalks', *National Bureau of Standards Miscellaneous Publication #112.*

Terpenning, Walter A. (1931) *Village and Open-Country Neighborhoods* (New York: Century).

True, Alfred C. (1937) *A History of Agricultural Experimentation and Research in the United States, 1607–1925* (Washington: Government Publishing Office), 34–40, 52–66, 172–7.

US Congress (1862) 'An Act Donating Public Lands to the Several States and Territories Which May Provide Colleges For the Benefit of Agriculture and the Mechanic Arts', *Statutes*, 12: 503.

US Congress (1862a) 'An Act to Establish A Department of Agriculture', *Statutes*, 12: 387.

US Congress (1887) 'An Act to Establish Agricultural Experiment Stations in Connection with the Colleges Established in the Several States Under the Provision of an Act Approved July 2, 1862, and of the Act Supplementary Thereto', *Statutes*, 24: 440.

US Congress (1890) 'An Act to Apply A Portion of the Proceeds of the Public Lands to the More Complete Endowment and Support of the Colleges For the Benefit of Agriculture and the Mechanic Arts Established Under the Provisions of An Act of Congress Approved July 2, 1862', *Statutes*, 26: 417.

US Congress (1906) 'An Act to Provide For An Increased Annual Appropriation For Agricultural Experiment Stations and Regulating the Expenditure Thereof', *Statutes*, 34: 63.

US Congress (1914) 'An Act to Provide For Cooperative Agricultural Extension Work Between the Agricultural Colleges in the Several States Receiving the Benefits of An Act of Congress Approved July 2, 1862, and of Acts Supplementary Thereto, And the United States Department of Agriculture', *Statutes*, 38: 372.

US Congress (1925) 'An Act to Authorize the More Complete Endowment of Agricultural Experiment Stations, and For Other Purposes', *Statutes*, 43: 970.

US Congress (1935) 'An Act to Provide For Research Into Basic Laws and Principles Relating to Agriculture and to Provide For the Further Development of Cooperative Agricultural Extension Work and the More Complete Endowment and Support of Land-Grant Colleges', *Statutes*, 49: 436.

US Congress (1946) 'An Act to Provide For Further Research Into Basic Laws and Principles Relating to Agriculture and to Improve and Facilitate the Marketing and Distribution of Agricultural Products', *Statutes*, 60: 1082.

Vance, Rupert B. (1929) *Human Factors in Cotton Culture. A Study in the Social Geography of the American South* (Chapel Hill: University of North Carolina Press).

Vogeler, Ingolf (1981) *The Myth of the Family Farm: Agribusiness Domination of United States Agriculture* (Boulder: Westview Press).

Waksman, Selman A. (1954) *My Life With Microbes* (New York: Simon and Schuster), 182–95, 208–42.

Ward, John William (1955) *Andrew Jackson, Symbol For An Age* (New York: Oxford).

Williams, James Mickel (1925) *Our Rural Heritage* (New York: Knopf).

Wiser, Vivian (1962) 'Maryland in the Early Land-Grant College Movement', *Agricultural History*, 36: 194–9.

Woodruff, H. Boyd (ed.) (1968) *Scientific Contributions of Selman A. Waksman* (New Brunswick: Rutgers University Press).

Part II

Thinking about Agricultural and Research Alternatives

3 Inefficiency and Structural Adjustment in American Agriculture: Who Will Quit and Why?

Carlisle Ford Runge[1]

INTRODUCTION

The agricultural economy is currently experiencing structural adjustment due to complex forces affecting commodity prices, farm costs, agricultural technology and asset values. These forces interact in many ways, presenting a confusing picture: although large numbers of farms are in or near bankruptcy, creating a general perception of farm crisis, many remain profitable. This has led some observers to conclude that the failing farms must be too small and technologically inefficient, and that market forces are culling the technologically weak from the herd. This view – which suggests that technological 'economies of large size' dominate farming – is widely held. Yet it is countered by the observation that many of the farms in deepest trouble are in fact quite large and technologically advanced.

This chapter will argue that size and technological efficiency are far less important than whether a given farm (of whatever size) is heavily indebted. Government policies exacerbating this debt position or imposing additional stress may in turn play as large a role as market forces in the future structure of American agriculture. The paper highlights the difference between technological forces (which may drive farmers from the sector due to their inability to keep pace with physical or engineering innovations) and financial forces (which operate through the prices of goods and assets in the market – see Yotopoulos and Nugent, 1976, Chapter 5). Technological efficiencies result from the optimal combination of engineering inputs (fertilizer, water, etc.), while financial efficiencies result from the optimal combination of financial resources (such as collateral and credit) in the purchase of goods and assets. While both sorts of efficiency are important to farm survival, it is useful to separate them for purposes of policy analysis.

Both theoretical and empirical evidence fail to support the contention that technological efficiencies *per se* have led to larger farms. This evidence suggests that increasing farm size is primarily the result of changing financial conditions, notably the relative cost of capital and labor, and the 'pecuniary' advantages enjoyed by larger farms. Despite these advantages, declining land prices caught up with heavily indebted farmers in the 1980s, many of whom were quite large. This is reflected by the changing debt–asset position, or 'leverage', of individual farm producers. As farm assets rose in value throughout the 1970s, increased acreage and increased borrowing were attractive, especially because inflation kept real interest levels low. Large farm debts were acquired, based on forecasts of continued increases in land values. These forecasts were wrong. Beginning in 1980–1, major devaluations in farm assets together with increases in real interest costs created extreme financial pressures for farmers who acquired large levels of debt to purchase these assets. Many of these farmers were young, well-educated, and technologically advanced. Hence, financial factors – generally the result of forecasting errors in which asset devaluations were not foreseen – dominate technological factors as a cause of structural change in agriculture.[2]

This result, if correct, has important policy implications for three reasons. First, it suggests that some technologically-advanced farm producers, both large and small, may be driven from the sector due to changes in financial conditions arising largely from outside agriculture or agricultural policy. One consequence appears to be to stabilize farm size. Second, the level of financial stress in agriculture will be highly skewed toward younger farmers, many of whom are more well-educated and more rapid adopters of new technology than older producers. Their quitting will therefore represent higher social costs in terms of foregone returns to investments in agricultural research and education. Third, if current trends continue, the remaining producers may be less indebted but also less technologically efficient than those that quit. This could lead to declines in the global competitiveness of American farmers.

This chapter is organized as follows. First, a discussion of farm size and the role of technical change in agriculture is presented, together with an analysis of financial stress arising especially from falling land values. Second, a specific empirical example is developed illustrating the significance of financial stress on even technologically efficient producers. Third, the implications of these results for policy are explored. The fourth section is a conclusion.

FARM SIZE AND TECHNICAL CHANGE IN AGRICULTURE

Farm size in the United States has grown substantially over the past half-century. From 1930 to 1980, land area per farm increased over 2.5 times, while the number of farms decreased from 6.3 to 2.7 million. Despite continued warnings of corporate takeovers of agriculture, American farms are likely to remain almost entirely family units, even if incorporated for tax reasons. As of 1979, only 2.4 per cent of all farm and ranchland in the United States was cultivated by nonfamily corporate farms (USDA, 1979). Increases in farm size have occurred primarily as a result of expansion purchases by some farmers from retiring or quitting farmers (see Emerson and Raup, 1985).

Despite rhetorical warnings of impending 'superfarms', the historical record suggests that the death of the family farm as an institution is exaggerated. Studies of the late nineteenth century 'Bonanza Farms' of the Red River Valley, in which 20 000 to 55 000 acres were cultivated using hired labor forces and equipment, indicated major inefficiencies (Briggs, 1932). These farms ceased to operate and were broken into family-sized units and sold in the early 1900s.

In an analysis of the sources of changing farm size, Kislev and Peterson (1982) developed an equilibrium theory of the size of the family farm which showed that out-migration (or quittings) of farm labor and the growth of farm size are two aspects of the same economic process. Increasing urban incomes serve as an incentive to leave farming; the remaining land is left to fewer but larger farms. Kislev and Peterson's analysis concentrated on three factors: input prices, nonfarm income, and technology, although it specifically excluded expectations of future land values and inflation as factors determining farm size.

> The dominance of the family unit in agriculture and of the large corporation in the nonfarm sector testifies to the lack of significant economies of scale in most farming operations and their existence in other industries. Owners of large amounts of wealth therefore

> invested their capital in the nonfarm sector. Where large farm enterprises ran into scale diseconomies they were subdivided into family units. The American family farm was preserved by ample nonfarm investment opportunities (Kislev and Peterson, p. 587).

Current rates of return in agriculture compared to the nonfarm sector suggest that the family farm continues to be unattractive to corporate raiders.

The primary factor responsible for the growth in farm size has not been off-farm corporate acquisition, but the change in the relative opportunity cost of farm labor in relation to that of farm machinery (see Kislev and Peterson, p. 588, Table 3). From 1930–70, the ratio of wage to machine costs increased 2.8 per cent per year. The increasing opportunity costs of farm labor – reflected by the relatively higher real wages available in the non-farm sector – induced substantial substitution of mechanical power, leading to increases in the ratio of machine to labor inputs by 4.8 per cent over the period (Kislev and Peterson, p. 590). The same forces which attracted labor out of agriculture also freed land resources and prompted substitution of larger mechanically-driven technology for labor. The farm family, able to cultivate larger acreage, purchased or rented the land left behind, and farm size grew. The process of technological change from 1930–70 thus involved the application of new engineering principles to land freed by off-farm migration. What made increases in farm size possible was the changing relative price of mechanical inputs (with biological inputs enhancing production per acre, but not farm size *per se*).

Between 1970 and 1976, however, the opportunity cost of farm labor relative to machine costs was reversed. This reversal (which has persisted) means that the ratio of wages in relation to machinery costs has fallen. This has created incentives for fewer and smaller farm machines. (The recent bankruptcy of the Steiger Tractor Company provides some evidence for this switch.) If the findings reported by Kislev and Peterson continue to hold, then farm size should stabilize and perhaps even decline (1982, p. 592).

In fact, farm size did not grow appreciably in the 1970s and early 1980s, supporting Kislev and Peterson's hypothesis. Although the national average grew from 352 acres in 1969 to 440 acres in 1982, this average was accompanied by a declining *rate* of increase, from 2.1 per cent from 1964–9 to −0.5 per cent from 1978–82. The general trend is also obscured by averages, since smaller hobby farms have increased in number as have very large farms, with the central tendency moving upward but at a steadily decelerating rate.

And the principal advantages of the very large farms may not be technological, but financial. In a recent report evaluating the impact of technology on farm structure, the Office of Technology Assessment noted that some of the principal advantages of very large farms are not technological, but are in buying and selling in large quantities and in access to credit. 'There is some evidence', the report noted, 'that inclusion of such pecuniary economies would lower the average production costs for large farm units and would shift the conclusion about the size of the most competitive farm' (OTA, 1985, pp. 27–8). Additional support for the importance of financial advantages accruing to large farms is provided for North Dakota small-grain production by Dalsted (1972) and for Texas cotton production and marketing by Smith *et al.* (1984). These advantages do not derive from superior physical or engineering factors, but from a different set of prices faced and financial resources available to very large farms.

If the explanation for farm size is not technological economies *per se*, then financial factors as well as expectations of future land values and inflation taken on added importance. All loomed large in the decision of some farmers to expand in the 1970s. Unfortunately, what may have seemed rational in 1975 proved disastrous in 1985. The University of Minnesota has compiled land market data which provides a useful basis for evaluating the unusual changes in the value of farm land assets during the 1970s and 1980s (see Figure 3.1). A time series of this data, expressed in both nominal and real terms (deflated by the Consumer Price Index), shows that the 1970s and early 1980s saw an historically unprecedented departure of real and nominal land values, and equally unprecedented increases and decreases in both. Throughout the period, most farmland purchase continued to be by expanding farmers, with the majority of sales to those within the same county and often the same township (Emerson and Raup, 1985). Indeed, the proportion of expansion buyers increased in Minnesota from approximately 55 per cent in 1970 to 79 per cent in 1984. In nominal terms, Minnesota farmland increased over fourfold in value between 1972 and 1981 before beginning on equally steep decline, ultimately resulting in a 26 per cent drop from 1985 to 1986. This increase and decline was repeated in varying degrees throughout

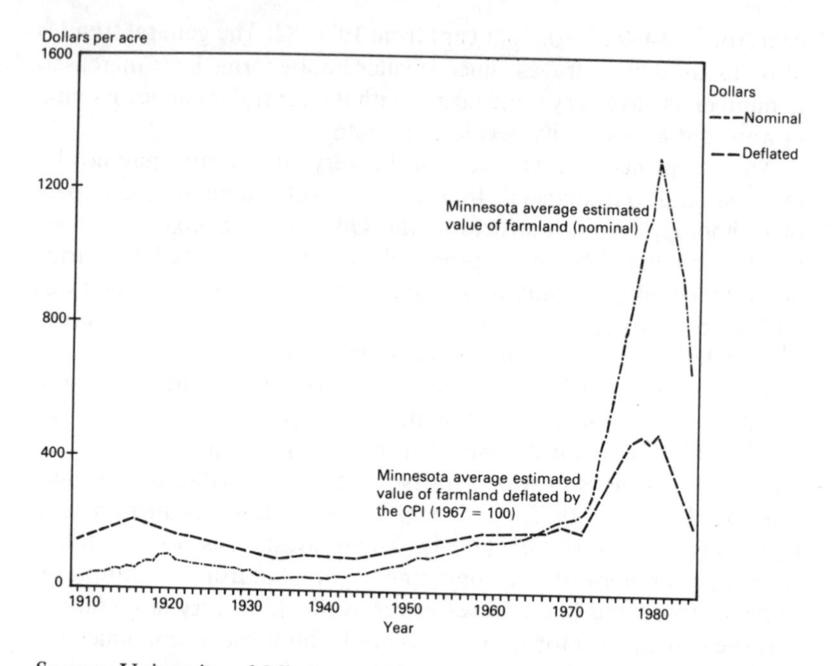

Source: University of Minnesota, Department of Agriculture and Applied Economics

Figure 3.1 Minnesota average estimated value per acre of farmland (deflated by the Consumer Price Index 1967 = 100)

the farmbelt, and has had disastrous effects on the debt–asset position of those who used land in the 1970s as collateral to acquire substantial additional debt.

In retrospect, the decision to base farm expansion on continued appreciation in land values was extremely unwise. Yet during the 1970s high levels of inflation, expanding export markets and low real interest rates made farm expansion – including land purchases – a seemingly rational strategy. Increases in farmland prices made entry into agriculture, in turn, increasingly expensive for beginning farmers who did not inherit a full complement of land and equipment. Many borrowed heavily to gain entry to the sector, which promised to reward the investment through asset appreciation if not profits.

Farmers were not alone in their bullish views of land assets. Farm lenders and some agricultural economists promoted expansion. Major investments were made in services and infrastructure by private investors, including the major grain companies, in the expectation that an export-driven expansion in the farm economy would continue. In addition, until 1979 most of the deposit instruments and rates charged borrowers at rural lending institutions were regulated, leading to borrowing which when combined with inflation sometimes made the real cost of funds negative.

In 1980–1 the bubble burst. A strengthening dollar, the 1979–80 grain embargo, and rapid increases in acreage planted to grain crops in Europe and Latin America led to steady erosion in export markets which has continued. Deregulation of rural credit markets led to rapid increases in nominal interest rates. Substantially lowered levels of inflation pushed the real costs of borrowed funds from negative levels in 1979 to historic highs by 1985. Increased real interest rates, supported by the huge federal borrowing needs required to finance $200 billion dollar deficits, attracted foreign investors to US Treasury securities. In order to purchase these instruments these investors required dollars, helping to reinforce the strength of the currency, which continued to float in late 1985 at levels substantially above those of 1981. This dynamic interaction reinforced the weakness of export markets, commodities prices, and land values.

In short, financial factors – together with erroneous expectations of land values and inflation – were fundamental to the motivation for farm expansion and debt acquisition. These factors are also fundamental to an understanding of the causes of the 'farm crisis'. This conclusion has been reinforced by a variety of recent studies (Boehlje, 1986; Bain and Paulson, 1986). In the main, this crisis appears to result from financial forces arising largely from outside agriculture – primarily monetary and fiscal policy and exchange rate adjustments. The financial picture of the farm sector which emerges is striking, both in terms of the magnitude of what is owed by farmers and the rapid deterioration of debt repayment capacity in the face of weak demand and falling commodities prices.

A survey of farm financial conditions revealed that in January 1984, 16.6 per cent of all farm operators were experiencing some sort of financial stress, indicated by debt–asset ratios in excess of 40 per cent. A year later, the proportion of farm operators under financial stress had more than doubled. In January 1985, farm operators with debt–asset ratios greater than 40 per cent held nearly two-thirds of a total farm debt of approximately $212 billion, while an estimated 34.4 per cent of this total was held by farm operators who faced extreme financial stress, with debt–asset ratios greater than 70 per cent (Barickman, 1985, p. 16). By January, 1986, a nine-state survey in the upper Midwest indicated that 52 per cent were in the financial stress category (see Bain and Paulson, 1986, p. 8). The overall balance

Table 3.1 Balance sheet of the farming sector as of 1 January 1977, 1981, 1984–6

	1977	*1981*	*1984*	*1985*[a]	*% change from 1984–5*	*1986*[b]	*% change from 1985–6*
Assets							
Real estate	496.4	828.4	764.5	749.2	−2.0	738.0	−1.5
Non-real estate	134.2	228.6	216.5	221.1	+2.0	224.4	+1.5
Financial assets	33.7	42.8	50.1	52.1	+3.9	54.4	+4.4
Total assets	664.1	1089.8	1031.1	1022.4	− .8	1016.8	− .5
Claims							
Liabilities							
Real estate	55.2	95.5	111.6	110.9	− .6	110.0	− .8
Nonreal estate	48.7	86.5	103.0	101.3	−1.6	101.8	+ .5
Total liabilities	103.9	182	214.7	212.1	−1.2	211.8	− .2
Owner equity	560.2	907.8	816.4	810.7	− .7	805.0	− .7
Total claims	664.1	1089.8	1031.1	1022.4	− .8	1016.8	− .5
Debt to asset ratio	15.6	16.7	20.8	20.7	− .5	20.8	.4

[a] preliminary.
[b] forecast.
Source: United States Department of Agriculture (1984), cited in Barickman (1985), p. 16.

Table 3.2 Debt–asset ratios of farmers, by age and region of the country (per cent); i.e. the average farmer under 35 years in the central United States owes $63 for every $100 of land and equipment owned

	Under 35	*35–44*	*45–54*	*55–64*	*65+*
Central	63	61	46	24	10
South	42	45	35	24	6
West	44	43	26	20	15
East	54	27	18	12	9

Source: Joint study by Food and Agricultural Policy Research Institute and the *Farm Journal*, March 1985.

sheet of the farm sector is shown in Table 3.1. A separate survey documented that this debt is heavily skewed to younger farm operators, who are generally better educated and more inclined to adopt new techniques of production (see Table 3.2). A final observation is that this debt is borne disproportionately by large farms (see below). In part, this is because these farms became large by assuming debt; in part, it is because large farms must finance higher investments in equipment and other expenses.

The general implication of this analysis is that financial factors may have dominated technological factors in the 1970s and early 1980s as the cause of large numbers of farm quits. Financial factors were the dominant reason for both farm expansion, including increases up to 1970, and subsequent farm failure, especially after 1981. If this hypothesis is accurate, then whether or not farm operators are technologically efficient (or large), many will quit due to financial inability to maintain positive net returns. If technological and financial inefficiency are positively related, those who fail to manage their operations well in one area may also fail to do so in the other. More disturbing, however, is the possibility that those who are now most financially stressed represent some of the most technologically efficient producers in the sector. To date, no systematic attempts have been made to distinguish these possibilities or to determine their relative validity. Some insight, however, can be gained from careful evaluation of farm management records, to which we now turn.

FARM MANAGEMENT

Data from the Minnesota farm management associations provide a picture of the relative impact of current financial conditions on different sizes and categories of farms (Eidman, 1985). In August 1984, survey data indicated that the percentage of operators with higher debt–asset ratios actually increased with size of farm. Thirty-one per cent of farms with annual sales of $40 000 to $199 999 and 56 per cent of operations with sales over $200 000 reported debt–asset ratios that exceeded 40 per cent. These ratios were highest in the export-dependent cash grain sector, concentrated in Southeastern and Southwestern Minnesota, where the average debt–asset ratios were 49 and 47 per cent respectively.

Simulations of some representative farms in Southwestern Minnesota were conducted by Eidman based on mid-1985 projections of the world and US economy. These simulations were designed to measure the impact of the complex forces discussed above on both a large (775 acre) crop farm and a medium (400 acre) crop–hog farm typical of the grains sector of the Upper Midwest. Crop yields on these representative farms reflect the application of enhanced technology. Yields on them have grown at rates 18 to 20 per cent above the county average in the Southwestern Farm Management District. Swine production is near the association average.

Utilizing the Food and Agricultural Policy Research Institute (FAPRI) model and projections from Wharton Econometrics in May and June 1985, the performance of these farms was simulated over the period 1985–9. This simulation was designed to capture the impact of monetary, fiscal and trade policy conditions as of late 1985. The assumptions used were:

1. Continued federal deficit spending in the range of $200 billion.
2. Real GNP growth of 2.6–3.5 per cent annually.
3. Unemployment decreases from 7.4 to 6.7 per cent.
4. GNP deflator increases from 3.7 to 4.9 per cent.
5. Three-month Treasury-bill rates averaging from 6.9 to 8.4 per cent.
6. Modest declines in the value of the dollar, equal to 16 per cent from 1986–9, with most of the decline coming during 1986–7,
7. Average annual gross domestic product (GDP) growth of 3.6 per cent in Latin America, 6.0 per cent in the Pacific Basin, 2.2 per cent in Europe, and 3.3 per cent in the centrally planned economies.

These assumptions were combined with farm support prices (deficiency payments and loan rates) set equal to those of 1984–5 (see Appendixes 1 and 2). This assumption is likely to slightly overstate farm income in light of the 1985 Farm Bill, which will lead to downward adjustments in loan rates. In addition, it was assumed that farmers could exercise the option to repay loans at the lower of the two values represented by the loan rate or the market price. The costs of the new Farm Bill are unlikely to allow the Secretary of Agriculture this discretion, again leading to slight overstatement of farm incomes in the simulations.

Two simulations were conducted. One was based on average management levels in comparison to the Farm Management Association as a whole. The other was based on a high level of management, equivalent to that of the most efficient producers in the association. These management levels, together with the yield assumptions cited above, provide a proxy for technological efficiency and its relative impact on farm profitability compared to financial factors. It should be emphasized that farmers participating in the surveys are generally an above-average sample, so that the simulations tend to grant the benefit of the doubt to the representative farms in terms of production efficiency. In order to test the impact of initial debt–asset position on farm survival a 0.30 ratio was compared to a 0.70 ratio. This comparison allows the relative effect of financial stress to be guaged.

Net farm income, adjustments in the value of farm equity (assets), and the probability of survival in each management category are shown in Tables 3.3, 3.4, and 3.5. With average levels of management, net farm income (Tables 3.3 and 3.4) improves over the 1986–9 period for both sizes of farms with a beginning debt–asset ratio of 0.30. However, the same farms experience negative net farm income with a beginning debt–asset ratio of 0.70, which persists over most of the period. The large crop farm shows a more sustained negative net loss than the combined operation.

With high management levels, a debt–asset ratio of 0.30 leads to increased net farm income over the period, moving from $31 668 to a healthy $51 430 for the crop farm and $20 283 to $27 702 for the crop–hog operation. With debt–asset ratios of 0.70, however, this improvement is substantially reduced on both operations. In either case, net farm incomes with an initial debt–asset position of 0.70 are likely to be very marginal, and will probably induce large numbers of quits.

When combined with the somewhat optimistic assumptions of farm

Table 3.3 Projected net farm income for the large crop farm (in $000)

Beginning debt–asset	*1985*	*1986*	*1987*	*1988*	*1989*
			Average management		
0.30	16 341	18 995	26 189	25 250	32 536
0.70	–17 532	–24 904	–14 456	–3 406	–4 098
			High management		
0.30	31 668	33 981	43 057	42 599	51 430
0.70	5 483	7 517	15 484	13 306	19 188

Source: Eidman (1985).

Table 3.4 Projected net farm income for the medium crop–hog farm (in $000)

Beginning debt–asset	*1985*	*1986*	*1987*	*1988*	*1989*
			Average management		
0.30	10 679	17 223	23 510	24 486	17 025
0.70	–3 798	2 551	7 933	7 617	–347
			High management		
0.30	20 283	26 261	33 299	34 505	27 702
0.70	5 274	11 731	18 695	19 661	12 580

Source: Eidman (1985).

price supports underlying the simulations, the conclusion that emerges is that the initial debt–asset position of the farm is a better indicator of the likelihood of who will quit than relative technological and managerial efficiency. The significance of financial relative to technological factors is thus given support.

In Table 3.5, specific estimates for the probability of survival of the two representative farms are presented. These estimates are based on beginning equity values, estimated decreases in equity due to land price declines, and the resulting probability that the farm will have debt–asset ratios in excess of 1.0 or 0.8 at the end of 1989. A debt–asset ratio of 1.0 is generally unsurvivable; a value of 0.8 places the survival of the operation in considerable jeopardy. As Table 3.5 indicates, with average management the large crop farm and the smaller crop–hog farm are both relatively certain to survive if initial debt–asset ratios are 0.30. If the initial debt–asset position is 0.70, however, the probability that the large crop farm will survive is

Table 3.5 Equity adjustments and probability of survival over the 1985–9 period

		Average Management			*High Management*		
Beginning Debt–asset 1/1/85	*Beginning equity 1/1/85 ($)*	*Equity 12/31/89 ($)*	*Probability of D/A < 1 (%)*	*Probability of D/A < 0.8 (%)*	*Equity 12/31/89 ($)*	*Probability of D/A < 1 (%)*	*Probability of D/A < 0.8 (%)*
			Large crop farm				
0.30	499 106	413 550	100	100	483 710	100	100
0.70	213 852	40 856	80	0	75 015	80	25
			Medium crop-hog farm				
0.30	274 363	235 634	100	100	283 267	100	100
0.70	116 737	4 477	55	0	51 217	100	25

Source: Eidman (1985).

reduced considerably, with only an 80 per cent probability of an ending debt–asset ratio less than 1, and no probability of a debt–asset less than 0.80. The crop–hog farm is placed in even greater danger by an initial debt–asset ratio of 0.70, with only a 55 per cent probability of an ending debt–asset ratio less than 1 and no probability of an ending position less than 0.80.

Shifts from average to high management do not affect the survival capacity of either farm in the initial 0.30 debt–asset position. Both farms remain relatively secure as before. High management somewhat improves the probability of survival at an initial debt–asset ratio of 0.70. This improvement is not striking, however, again suggesting the relative importance of financial factors for farm survival. The large crop farm continues to show only an 80 per cent chance of an ending debt–asset ratio less than 1, and its chances of an ending ratio less than 0.80 are now only 25 per cent. The crop–hog farm shows a certain ending debt–asset ratio less than 1, but only a 25 per cent chance of a ratio less than 0.80.

These results are driven largely by projected changes in the value of land (Eidman, 1985). Regardless of technological efficiency, and despite optimistic assumptions about support prices, the financial impacts of land price devaluations on farm finances continue to dominate the survival capacity of farms in both large and medium size categories.

SOME POLICY IMPLICATIONS

While the data presented above are in no way conclusive, they provide some insight into the impact of agricultural and general economic policy on the future structure of American agriculture. Three main implications emerge from the analysis.

First, if it is true that monetary, fiscal and exchange rate policies have been the main cause of farm bankruptcies, then the 1985 Farm Bill, acting alone, can do little to alleviate the stresses being felt in the agricultural sector. Instead, three financial factors emerge as of paramount importance to farm recovery. First, without substantial reductions in real interest rates – either via reduced borrowing costs, increased inflation, or both – financial pressures will continue. Second, land value declines will place those with high debt–asset ratios in an increasingly tenuous position, encouraging the most highly-leveraged producers to quit farming, at least in the short run. Because these farmers are disproportionately made up of large producers, downward pressure on farm size can be expected to persist for a time. Third, exports will continue to dominate the demand for agricultural commodities, especially in the grains sector. Weak demand for US agricultural exports will in turn contribute to increases in surplus stocks, reducing world market prices and raising the costs of US farm price support programs. These program costs will continue to fuel a federal budget deficit that puts direct upward pressure on interest rates and indirect upward pressure on exchange rates, exacerbating the financial difficulties identified above. If past trends in farm land purchases are any guide, those farms with lower leverage positions will purchase farm land and equipment from neighbors. However, in the absence of renewed strength in commodities prices, the financial rewards to farm expansion are likely to continue to be small. If, given relative costs of labor and mechanical inputs, there are no clear technological economies to larger farm size, there seems little reason to suppose that farms will grow as rapidly as in the 1970s. Instead, land will be retired from production, notably through government acreage and conservation set-aside programs.

A second implication concerns the impact of current trends on the age distribution of farm operators. The data reported above indicate that many of the farmers that took on debt in the 1970s and 1980s were younger and generally better educated. The burden of downward price adjustments in land values fell with particular force on this group. Many of these farmers were the products of the land-grant colleges, educated in the ways of expansive, technologically sophisticated, export-oriented agriculture. If large numbers now quit the sector, it will constitute a substantial loss of human capital and technological expertise, possibly leading to a 'missing generation' in American farming. Although many economists have argued that excess capacity in the farm sector requires large numbers of quits to restore equilibrium, the question of *who* will quit has not been squarely addressed. The result can be to lower the productivity of the sector as a whole. If the quitters are drawn disproportionately from a group of highly educated and technologically sophisticated producers who are also heavily in debt, the social costs in terms of foregone returns to investment in agricultural research and education may be substantial. This argument is reinforced by the generally high rates of return resulting from these investments (Ruttan, 1982).

A final implication for policy concerns the future competitiveness of American farmers. If the burden of adjusting to new financial conditions in agriculture falls on those most heavily indebted, and these producers are disproportionately made up of young, well-educated and technologically advanced producers, the effect may be to erode the competitive advantage represented by the level and quality of human capital in American agriculture. This human capital resource is as important as soils, water, climate and infrastructure in guaranteeing long-term competitiveness in world markets. The foregone benefits of this loss of competitiveness are extremely difficult to estimate, and the costs of preventing these producers from bankruptcy may not justify them. These issues are beyond the scope of this chapter, which has attempted to diagnose the nature of structural changes in agriculture, rather than provide specific prescriptions.

CONCLUSION

The causes of the farm financial crisis are complex, involving trends largely outside the reach of traditional agricultural policy instruments. This chapter has provided an argument for the importance of financial factors in the current farm crisis. Interest rates, input costs, and expectations of land values and inflation dominate technological change as an explanation for farm size and farm quits. These financial factors may also help to explain the lack of strong incentives to increase farm acreage in the near future. The impact of these factors requires a new orientation for agricultural policy, focused less on agricultural programs then on fiscal, monetary and trade policy. Like other export-dependent, interest-rate-sensitive sectors of the economy, American agriculture is in danger of losing its international competitiveness. The burden of current policies appears to fall disproportionately on younger, more well-educated producers, leading to reduced returns to previous investments in human capital in agriculture.

Unfortunately, comparatively little attention has been given by agricultural policy analysts to the question of whether those who quit farming will leave behind the group of farmers most capable of advancing the overall competitiveness of the agricultural sector. If current trends are allowed to continue, financial adjustments may erode American agriculture's advantage, which rests in large part on its human capital base.

APPENDIX 1

Variable loan rate policy proposal

Assumes:
1. Target prices and loan rates are set at minimum 1984–5 levels, and
2. Farmers have the option of repaying loans at the loan rate or at a market price, whichever is lower.

Table 3.A1 Values for selected parameters

	1985–6	*1986–7*	*1987–8*	*1988–9*	*1989–90*
Loan rate, corn	2.55	2.55	2.55	2.55	2.55
Target rate, corn	3.03	3.03	3.03	3.03	3.03
Set aside, corn	10%	20%	20%	20%	20%
Loan rate, soybeans	5.02	5.02	5.02	5.02	5.02
Farm price, S.W. MN					
Corn ($/bu)	2.35	1.91	2.10	2.32	2.34
Soybeans ($/bu)	4.99	4.83	5.22	5.97	6.03
Hogs ($/cwt)	45.00	43.00	45.00	47.00	45.00

APPENDIX 2

Description of Southwestern Minnesota farm

	Large crop farm	*Medium-sized crop-hog farm*
Cropland owned (acres)	500	200
Cropland leased (acres)	275	160
Breeding herd (no. of sows)	–	48
Market value of assets 1/1/85		
Land	$531 160	$217 980
Other real estate	70 634	80 000
Farm machinery	109 338	79 585
Livestock for breeding	–	9 822
Total	$711 130	$387 387

continued on p. 50

APPENDIX 2, *continued*

	Large crop farm	*Medium-sized crop-hog farm*
Labor supply		
Family labor (full-time equivalents)	1.5	1.0
Hired labor (full-time equivalents)	.25	.03
Average management levels		
Corn yield (bu/acre)	106.5	106.5
Soybeans yield (bu/acre)	35.2	35.2
Slaughter hogs (direct cost/sow)	–	$722
(bu. corn/sow)	–	180.3
High management level		
Corn yield (bu/acre)	117.2	117.2
Soybean yield (bu/acre)	38.7	38.7
Slaughter hogs (direct cost/sow)	–	$686
(bu. corn/sow)	–	171.3

Notes

1. My thank to Willis Peterson and Vern Eidman for discussions and suggestions in the course of preparing this chapter. The policy analysis here and reponsibility for its errors and omissions belong to me alone.
2. This argument does not suggest that other causes (such as the life-cycle of individual farmers) may not also be important. The focus here is restricted to these major causes due to their popularity as explanations.

References

Bain, Ian R. M., and Jo Ann Paulson (1986) 'Financial Stress in Agriculture: Its Causes and Extent', *Minnesota Agricultural Economist*, Special Issue no. 1, 651 (Minnesota Extension Service, University of Minnesota).

Barickman, Nancy E. (1985) 'Summaries and Comparisons of Farm Financial Stress Surveys: National, Regional and State', Department of Economics (Iowa State University, Ames, Iowa, 7 May 1985).

Boehlje, Michael (1986) 'Farm Financial Stress and the US Farm Crisis: Origins and Dimensions of the Problem', Staff Paper P86–22 (Department of Agricultural and Applied Economics, University of Minnesota).

Briggs, Harold E. (1932) 'Early Bonanza Farming in the Red River Valley of the North', *Agricultural History* 6 (Jan.): 23–7.

Dalsted, Norman L. (1972) *Pecuniary Economies of Farm Size in Northern East Central North Dakota* (M.S. thesis, North Dakota State University, Fargo, North Dakota).

Eidman, Vernon (1985) 'Description of Minnesota Agriculture', briefing before the Minnesota Senate Committee on Agriculture and Natural Resources, 21 November 1985 (University of Minnesota, Institute of Agriculture, Forestry and Home Economics, St Paul, Minnesota).

Emerson, Carolyn J. and Philip M. Raup (1985) *The Minnesota Rural Real Estate Market in 1984* (Economic Report ER 85–1, Department of Agricultural and Applied Economics, University of Minnesota, St Paul, Minnesota).

Kislev, Yoav and Willis Peterson (1982) 'Prices, Technology, and Farm Size', *Journal of Political Economy* 90 (3): 578–95.

Office of Technology Assessment (OTA) (1985) Congress of the United States, *Technology, Public Policy, and the Changing Structure of American Agriculture: A Special Report for the 1985 Farm Bill* (Washington, DC, OTA–F–272, US Government Printing Office).

Ruttan, V. W. (1982) *Agricultural Research Policy* (Minneapolis, University of Minnesota Press).

Smith, Edward *et. al.* (1984) *Cost and Pecuniary Economies in Cotton Production and Marketing: A Study of Texas Southern High Plains Cotton Producers* (Texas A & M University, Agricultural Experiment Station Bulletin B–1475, College Station, Texas).

US Department of Agriculture (1984) *Agricultural Finance Situation and Outlook*, ERS, AFO–25, December 1984 (Washington, DC, US Government Printing Office).

US Department of Agriculture (1979) 'Who Owns the Land? A Preliminary Report of a U.S. Land Ownership Survey', ESCS, Report 70 (Washington, DC, Government Printing Office).

Yotopoulos, P. A. and J. B. Nugent (1976) *Economics of Development* (New York, Harper and Row).

4 Moving from Yesterday's Agricultural Technology: Alternative Farming Systems in Perspective

I. Garth Youngberg

INTRODUCTION

The 1983 magazine article was entitled 'Updating Organic Farming: New Looks at Old Ways'. It began with these words: 'There's a fairly common belief in most agricultural circles today that farming without chemicals is horse-and-buggy technology – something that only starry-eyed "back-to-the-landers" do on little weed-infested patches of ground'. On the contrary, however, the author quickly noted that he and the magazine's other editors, while preparing the article, had 'talked to many farmers who are producing good crops on large acreages without using any pesticides or synthetic fertilizers'. The writer went on to point out that modern organic farmers are 'good managers. They use modern equipment. Their fields are not overgrown with weeds or riddled by insects. Generally, their yields are somewhat below average for the area, but so are production costs' (Kessler, 1983).

These observations are noteworthy for a number of reasons. First, the article did not appear in the alternative agriculture press. It was written by Karl Kessler, veteran regional editor for *The Furrow*, a highly respected conventional farm magazine published by Deere and Company and distributed to conventional farmers through lists provided by local John Deere machinery dealers. Second, while the advocates and practitioners of alternative agriculture have long known of its modern technical character, economic performance, and overall level of success, this article, like scores of others that have appeared recently in the conventional farm press (Risser, 1984; Swoboda, 1984; Holmberg, 1985; Henkes, 1985), reveals conventional agriculture's growing interest in the potential role of alternative farming systems in modern production agriculture. Third, the article addressed a number of the lingering misconceptions and misunderstandings which continue to impede the widescale adoption of alternative farming systems in the USA and abroad. Many conventional farmers, agricultural scientists and policy-makers continue to hold the mistaken view that alternative agriculture represents a return to the farm structure and low-yield, labor-intensive production technologies and practices of the 1930s and 1940s. This erroneous and negative symbolism constitutes a major barrier to the thoughtful development of an integrated and comprehensive program of public education, agricultural research, and other policy-related programs that will be necessary if alternative farming systems are ever to compete on a wide scale with conventional energy and chemical intensive systems of food and fiber production.

In the pages that follow, I will attempt (a) to review and summarize the character and consequences of conventional agricultural production practices and farm structure trends over the past four decades or so, (b) to show that a growing number of farmers, agricultural scientists and policy-makers are beginning to investigate how, and to what degree, alternative farming systems can effectively address at least some of the problems that have come to plague American agriculture, and (c) to analyze the future prospects for the widescale adoption of low-input farming technologies in the United States.

The scope of this discussion on the subject 'alternative agriculture' is broad and yet definite. The word 'alternative' is used here as an umbrella term that embraces a number of more specific terms, all of which refer to various alternative agriculture production systems. For example, words such as 'organic', 'ecological', 'biological', 'regenerative', 'natural', 'sustainable' and 'agroecological' are all used by various alternative agriculture groups and spokespersons. In varying degrees, all of these approaches and 'schools of thought' are designed to help foster an agricultural system that is both economically profitable and environmentally stable. The term 'alternative' denotes a spectrum of low-chemical, resource- and energy-conserving and resource-efficient farming systems and technologies. Thus, throughout this paper, the definition of organic agriculture developed by the USDA Study Team on Organic Agriculture will be used synonymously with the word alternative. According to the Study Team:

> Organic farming is a production system which avoids or largely excludes the use of synthetically compounded fertilizers, pesticides, growth regulators, and livestock feed additives. To the

maximum extent feasible, organic farming systems rely upon crop rotations, crop residues, animal manures, legumes, green manures, off-farm organic wastes, mechanical cultivation, mineral-bearing rocks, and aspects of biological pest control to maintain soil productivity and tilth, to supply plant nutrients, and to control insects, weeds, and other pests (USDA, 1980).

Having acknowledged the fact that agricultural production practices mix and blend countless variations along a spectrum ranging from those that avoid or largely exclude the use of agricultural chemicals, to those that rely on their heavy and even indiscriminate use, it is nonetheless important to recognize that alternative farming systems, in the final analysis, differ substantially from their energy- and chemical-intensive conventional counterparts.

It is important for the reader to bear several points in mind. Alternative agriculture is not a panacea for the complex economic and environmental problems that currently afflict modern production agriculture. Nor do alternative systems and technologies offer a quick fix for these interrelated problems. Moreover, alternative approaches would not be universally adopted by American farmers even in an ideal policy environment.

Having said this, however, it is equally important for policy analysts and policy-makers to realize that alternative farming systems work. These technologies and approaches are being used successfully on thousands of large-scale commercial farms in the USA (USDA, 1980). These low-input systems reduce production costs, enhance environmental quality and, perhaps most important of all, do so without the need for huge government subsidies. Given the painful and seemingly intractable nature of the present American 'farm problem', coupled with the policy community's growing disenchantment with traditional 'farm programs', it may now behove agricultural policy-makers, and those who would influence them, to investigate objectively and thoroughly the proper role and future potential for these alternatives to yesterday's and today's conventional agricultural technology.

THE CHARACTER AND CONSEQUENCES OF AGRICULTURAL TECHNOLOGY AND FARM STRUCTURE TRENDS: A BRIEF REVIEW

Over the past forty years, particularly in the past twenty-five years or so, American agricultural production practices have been substantially altered. During the same period the structure of American agriculture also has been transformed in equally fundamental respects. Large-scale, highly specialized, capital- and energy-intensive farms now dominate US agriculture. Monocultural cropping systems, particularly of cash grains, large confinement animal feeding operations and fossil fuel-based production technologies, especially the heavy use of synthetically compounded fertilizers and pesticides, have been widely adopted by America's farmers. For the most part, these structural and technological trends have impeded the development of diversified, biologically based, resource-conserving farming systems. However, it is important to note that much of the US's contemporary agricultural abundance is directly attributable to the widescale adoption of these modern technologies.

While acknowledging the benefits of these conventional energy- and chemical-intensive technologies on overall food and fiber production, a growing number of scientists and policy-makers are now voicing concern over the increasingly heavy dependence of conventional agriculture on fossil fuel energy and the adverse effects on environmental quality and long-term agricultural sustainability caused by increased soil erosion and the excessive use of agricultural chemicals (Papendick *et al.*, 1986; Brown and Wolf, 1984; Duda and Johnson, 1985). According to Papendick *et al.* (1986), 'the evidence indicates that both erosion and chemical pollution of soil and water have been accelerated by modern farming practices. Particularly responsible was the shift in recent decades away from soil conserving crop rotations to intensive monoculture of grain or continuous row cropping systems accompanied by intensive tillage practices'. There also is mounting concern over the possibly harmful effects of excessive pesticide use and inorganic fertilization on food quality and safety and human and animal health.

Partly in response to these and other questions, in 1979 the US Department of Agriculture (USDA) appointed a study team on organic farming. The team was asked to assess the nature and extent of alternative farming systems in the USA, see how such systems might help address these mounting concerns, and set forth a research and education agenda that could help meet the needs of an alternative system. In the study team's *Report and Recommendations on Organic Farming* (USDA, 1980) the following concerns regarding the present system of US agriculture were cited:

1. Increased cost and uncertain availability of energy and farm chemicals.
2. Increased resistance of weeds to herbicides and insects to pesticides.
3. Decline in soil productivity from erosion and the accompanying loss of soil organic matter and plant nutrients.
4. Pollution of surface waters with agricultural chemicals and sediment.
5. Destruction of wildlife, bees, and beneficial insects by pesticides.
6. Hazards to human and animal health from pesticides and feed additives.
7. Detrimental effects of agricultural chemicals on food quality.
8. Depletion of finite reserves of concentrated plant nutrients (for example, phosphate rock).
9. Decrease in number of farms, particularly family-type farms, and disappearance of localized and direct marketing systems.

The following year another major Departmental report (USDA, 1981) detailed the major historical and ongoing structural trends in US agriculture. These included: (a) increases in average farm size, (b) further concentration of farm sales and assets, (c) growth in the capital intensity of agriculture, and (d) increased mechanization and specialization of farm enterprises. The trends and developments of the past five years (e.g. growing scientific disquiet over agriculturally related environmental degradation, accelerating economic pressures on the family farm, and faltering farm exports), have lent credence to the projections and concerns noted in both of these reports.

WHAT ROLE FOR ALTERNATIVE AGRICULTURE?

In light of these and other agriculturally related problems and concerns, a growing number of agricultural policy-makers, policy analysts, agricultural scientists and conventional farmers are beginning to show a genuine interest in alternative agriculture. For example, farm enterprise diversification, including specialty crops and direct marketing, is now experiencing renewed interest within conventional agricultural circles. Similarly, the benefits of mixed cropping systems which include legume hay and other nitrogen-fixing crops such as peas and lentils, are also being explored as a way to stabilize and enhance farm income, reduce production costs, and make agricultural ecosystems more sustainable in the long term.

These and similar questions are now being examined in a rapidly proliferating number of workshops, field days, symposia, conferences, formal academic and government studies, and congressional hearings. Researchers, policy-makers and farmers want answers to the following kinds of questions: Is alternative agriculture a viable option for America's farmers? What are the macroeconomic implications of alternative farming systems? What are the structural implications? What are the major agronomic, economic, political and structural obstacles to the widescale adoption of alternative systems? What are the research and education requirements of an alternative system? Because the growing effort to answer these and other questions has been documented elsewhere (e.g. Parr *et al.*, 1983; Youngberg and Buttel, 1984; Risser, 1984), the following selected examples are intended only to highlight this new found interest in the character and potential of alternative agriculture.

1. In 1980, the USDA published its cautiously optimistic *Report and Recommendations on Organic Farming*. Approximately 50 000 copies of that report have been distributed world-wide. It has been translated into several foreign languages. This *Report* helped focus scientific attention on the potential role of organic agriculture in modern production agriculture; it also helped to dispel a number of common misperceptions about these systems and the people who employ them (USDA, 1980).
2. In 1981, *Science* magazine (Lockeretz *et al.*, 1981) published an overview article which summarized the generally positive findings from the five-year organic farming study conducted in the 1970s by Washington University's Center for the Biology of Natural Systems.
3. In 1981, the Rodale Research Center started a major long-term conversion experiment on the transition from chemical-intensive to organic farming systems. The work of the Center is now attracting widespread interest among US and Canadian scientists. In 1984, USDA's Agricultural Research Service (ARS) placed a full-time research scientist at the Center. Early reports indicate that this initiative may provide the organizational framework for a permanent, joint public/private effort to coordinate ongoing and planned research related to alternative agriculture.

4. In 1983, North Carolina State University began offering a regular, credit course entitled 'Alternative Agricultural Systems'. Scientists and students in NC State's Soils Department are also conducting a major organic farming literature review.
5. Scientists and students at the University of Maryland organized a special course on alternative cropping systems during fall term, 1984. A number of other universities (e.g. Washington State University and the University of Minnesota) have undertaken similar efforts in recent years.
6. The 1981 Annual Meeting of the American Society of Agronomy sponsored a full-day symposium entitled, 'Organic Farming: Current Technology and Its Role in a Sustainable Agriculture'. Subsequently, the Society published the symposium proceedings (Bezdicen *et al.*, 1984).
7. The Board on Agriculture and Renewable Resources of the National Research Council (NRC), one of the most prestigious agricultural research organizations in the United States, currently has a sixteen-month study underway on the role of alternative farming systems in modern production agriculture. The study will (a) summarize existing knowledge pertaining to the potential benefits of alternative agriculture, (b) examine how these systems can help to achieve national soil conservation and supply-management goals, and (c) develop a prioritized research agenda.
8. The University of Nebraska's Institute of Agriculture and Natural Resources held its fifth annual Alternative Farming Systems Field Day and Farm Tour in 1985.
9. In 1984 Michigan State University, in co-operation with the International Federation of Organic Agriculture Movements (IFOAM) and Rodale Press, hosted a three-day interdisciplinary scientific symposium entitled 'Sustainable Agriculture and Integrated Farming Systems'. The proceedings from that conference are now available (Edens *et al.*, 1985).
10. The 1985 farm bill included an authorizing provision which directs the US Department of Agriculture to conduct a five-year research project on thirty-six selected farms throughout the US. Twelve of these on-farm studies would gather information on established organic operations, twelve would involve an investigation of the transition from a chemically intensive to an organic system of production, and twelve would be conducted on conventional farms. A number of land grant universities have expressed interest in participating in these on-farm studies, and a large

number of conventional farm organizations and environmental groups are supportive of this legislation.

11. The Institute for Alternative Agriculture embarked upon publication of a refereed journal in 1986. The *American Journal of Alternative Agriculture* is designed to provide an academic forum and suitable publication outlet for research scientists, students and others who are interested in alternative agriculture. Twenty-seven leading agricultural and policy scientists serve on the journal's editorial board.

While most agricultural research, education and policy-making activity continues to revolve around conventional, high-input technologies and management systems, these examples clearly illustrate that the agricultural establishment is no longer monolithic on these issues. This author, for example, writing in 1978, could find few major examples of conventional agriculture's interest or involvement in alternative farming systems (Youngberg, 1978). Today, such examples abound. Although the overall level of commitment to alternative agriculture remains relatively small compared to that which is devoted to conventional approaches, it is important to realize that a substantial and recognizable shift in the sympathies and interests of conventional agriculturists toward alternative techniques has occurred over the past five to ten years. Alternative farming systems are no longer dismissed as being frivolous or un-American.

FUTURE PROSPECTS: OPPORTUNITIES AND OBSTACLES

Despite the increasing interest in alternative agriculture noted above, a number of socio-economic factors and public agricultural policies continue to pose barriers to the widescale adoption of these alternative production systems. Structural trends in US agriculture continue to run counter to the development of alternative approaches. The growth in energy and capital intensity, greater specialization, and the trend toward larger average farm sizes over the past four decades, have combined to create an industrial form of agriculture in the US. Public agricultural tax, credit and commodity policy, low relative energy prices, agricultural research and education policy, and the decentralized, competitive character of agriculture as an industry, including the cost-price squeeze and short-term planning horizons, have also contributed to recent farm structure trends (Youngberg and Buttel, 1984). Should these trends continue, it will be very difficult, if not impossible, for the agroecosystem diversity associated with alternative agriculture to develop on a wide scale. However, as Ford Runge suggests elsewhere in this book, the current financial crisis in agriculture may be associated with a reversal in the trend toward larger, capital-intensive farms, and also the innovative farmers who had been moving agriculture in that direction. It is to be hoped that there remain innovative farmers capable of moving back toward low-input agriculture.

Public agricultural research policy must also address more fully the needs of alternative agriculture if large numbers of conventional farmers are to adopt these systems. However, short-term pressures on the public agricultural research system will probably preclude any substantial short-term redirection of research priorities toward alternative agriculture (Buttel and Youngberg, 1985). This is so for several reasons. First, both public and private research policy is now placing a great deal of emphasis on biotechnologies in agriculture, partly as a response to concerns over the US competitive positions in science and technology, and partly over recent signs that the rate of productivity increase in American agriculture is beginning to plateau (Cochrane, 1979). Many believe that agricultural biotechnologies are important, not only for ensuring US competitiveness in agriculture, but also for improving the technological base of other industries. For example, the so-called Winrock Report (Rockefeller Foundation, 1982) argued for a greater emphasis on basic biological research. These new research priorities tend to de-emphasize work in agroecology and other applied research important to the future development of alternative farming systems. Agricultural biotechnology and the needs and objectives of an alternative agriculture system are not necessarily mutually exclusive. For example, the development of bacterial pesticides would enhance environmental quality and make it possible for more farmers to adopt alternative approaches. But some other potential applications of biotechnology such as herbicide-tolerant plants would tend to have negative implications for the development of alternative farming systems (Buttel and Youngberg, 1983). Second, the growing research and education emphasis on conservation tillage, fostered in part by the continued reliance on cash grain exports to prop up farm income, will tend to encourage the increased use of monocultural cropping systems and the heavy use of pesticides.

Despite the growing emphasis on biotechnology in agriculture, it is important to note that many applied agricultural scientists remain open to working with alternative agriculturalists: they recognize the value of low-input, systems-oriented research. Many would like to bolster political support for applied research programs, and they see the alternative agriculture constituency as an important resource in this regard.

Scientists wishing to organize and conduct long-range interdisciplinary research on alternative systems will have to overcome the disciplinary basis of university departmental organization which militates against these kinds of research projects (Lukens, 1984). They will also have to deal with the definitional ambiguities surrounding alternative agriculture. The plethora of poorly defined terms (terms that will carry negative symbolism for many conventional agriculturists) continues to frustrate and confuse both the proponents and skeptics of alternative farming systems. Furthermore, these ambiguities make it possible for the opponents of alternative agriculture to claim that the needed research is being done, and that ample information on alternative systems is readily available to producers.

In conclusion, the future role and scope of alternative agriculture is uncertain. The expansion of these low-input technologies will be conditioned by a myriad of factors: farm structure trends, public agricultural research and education policy, agricultural tax, credit, commodity, conservation, export policy, the future cost and availability of energy, environmental constraints, and consumer attitudes and beliefs regarding the quality and safety of the food supply. Taken together, this complex technical and political milieu has unpredictable implications for the future of alternative agriculture. However, increased public pressure to conserve soil and water, to protect the environment, to lower farm production costs and enhance farm income, and find workable and affordable solutions for the continuing demise of the family farm, will undoubtedly generate increased interest in alternative farming and marketing systems. As pointed out here, for the first time since the early post-Second World War period, proponents of alternative agriculture now include important elements of the agricultural establishment. How fast these numbers grow will depend, at least to some degree, on the alternative agriculture movement's ability to capitalize on agriculture's altered physical, economic and policy environment.

References

Bezdicek, D. F., Power, J. F., Keeney, D. R. and Wright, M. J. (eds) (1984) *Organic farming: Current technology and its role in a sustainable agriculture* (Madison, WI: American Society of Agronomy).
Brown, L. R. and Wolf, E. C. (1984) *Soil erosion: Quiet crisis in the world economy*. Worldwatch Paper 60 (Washington, D.C.: Worldwatch Institute).
Buttel, F. H. and Youngberg, I. G. (1983) 'Implications of biotechnology for the development of sustainable agricultural systems' in W. Lockeretz (ed.), *Environmentally sound agriculture*. (pp. 377–400) (New York: Praeger).
Buttel, F. H. and Youngberg, I. G. (1985) 'Sustainable agricultural research and technology transfer: Socio-political opportunities and constraints' in T. C. Edens, C. Fridgen, and S. Battenfield (eds), *Sustainable agriculture and integrated farming systems: Conference proceedings* (East Lansing: Michigan State University Press).
Cochrane, W. W. (1979) *The development of American agriculture* (Minneapolis: University of Minnesota Press).
Duda, A. M. and Johnson, R. J. (1985) 'Cost-effective targeting of agricultural nonpoint-source pollution controls' *Journal of Soil & Water Conservation* 4:108–111.
Edens, T. C., C. Fridgen, and S. Battenfield (eds) (1984) *Sustainable Agriculture & Integrated Farming Systems: Conference proceedings* (East Lansing: Michigan State University Press).
Henkes, R. (1985) 'The mainstreaming of alternative agriculture' *The Furrow* 90:10–13.
Holmberg, M. (1985) 'What you can learn from organic farmers' *Successful Farming* 83:22–23.
Kessler, K. (1983) 'Updating organic farming: New looks at old ways' *The Furrow* 88:11–13.
Lockeretz, W., Shearer, G. and Kohl, D. H. (1981) 'Organic farming in the corn belt' *Science* 211:540–547.
Lukens, J. R. (1984) 'Lack of integrated studies of farming systems hampers transfer of research on organic farms' M.S. thesis, Department of Agronomy, Kansas State University, Manhattan.
Papendick, R. I., Elliott, L. F. and Dahlgren, R. B. (1986) 'Environmental consequences of modern production agriculture: How can alternative agriculture address these issues and concerns?' *American Journal of Alternative Agriculture* 1:3–11.
Parr, J. F., Papendick, R. I. and Youngberg, I. G. (1983) 'Organic farming in the United States: Principles and perspectives' *Agro-Ecosystems* 8:183–201.
Rockefeller Foundation (1982) *Science for agriculture* (New York: Rockefeller Foundation).
Risser, J. (1984) 'Organic farming' *Des Moines Register*, Five-Part Series. June 10–14.
Swoboda, R. (1984) 'Low cost farming' *Wallaces Farmer* 109:12–13.

US Department of Agriculture (1980) *Report and recommendations on organic farming* (Washington, D.C.).
US Department of Agriculture (1981) *A time to choose* (Washington, D.C.).
Youngberg, I. G. and Buttel, F. H. (1984) 'Public policy and socio-political factors affecting the future of sustainable farming systems' in D. F. Bezdicek, J. F. Power, D. R. Keeney, and M. J. Wright (eds), *Organic farming: Current technology and its role in a sustainable agriculture* (Madison, WI: American Society of Agronomy).
Youngberg, I. G. (1978) 'Alternative agriculturalists: Ideology, politics, and prospects' in D. F. Hadwiger and W. P. Browne (eds), *The new politics of food*. (pp. 227–246) (Lexington: Lexington Books).

Part III

Current Political Issues and Conflict

5 Political Support for National and International Public Research

Hemchandra Gajbhiye and
Don F. Hadwiger[1]

THE NEED FOR INTERNATIONAL AGRICULTURAL RESEARCH

Adequate food for the world's population over the next two decades requires an increase in production of 3 to 4 per cent a year in most developing countries and an average increase in yield on already cropped lands of no less than 2 per cent yearly (World Bank, 1981). Increases in productivity in the past 100 years have come largely from the application of science-based farm technology and from changes in management and inputs developed through organized research. Because most countries are now running out of good agricultural land, it is essential that agricultural research generates new technology that will permit higher yielding crops and livestock production if malnutrition is to be reduced, increased food costs are to be avoided, and economic growth not threatened.

One of the ways to increase food production may be through the direct transfer of technology from one country to another. For the developing countries, however, the vast majority of which have tropical or subtropical climates, the effective transfer of technology from the developed countries is frequently difficult. Agricultural research that is needed in any particular country is determined in part by the unique soils and climatic, social and other conditions.

Therefore, the particular research needs of developing countries must be met mainly through research carried out in agroclimatic and socio-economic circumstances in which the resulting technology is to be employed. A recent review by the International Food Policy Research Institute covering some sixty-five developing countries suggests that serious problems of understaffing in agricultural research exist, particularly in low-income countries that have important agriculture sectors. Among the low-income countries, the equivalent of only 0.26 per cent of the agricultural gross domestic product was spent on agricultural research in 1975. In middle-income and high-income developing countries, which generally have relatively smaller agriculture sectors, the equivalent of 0.42 per cent and 0.33 per cent, respectively, was spent. The comparable figures in developed countries are in the 1–2 per cent range. In terms of money spent on research for each person whose livelihood depends on agriculture, disparities are even more striking. The low-income developing countries spend $0.26 annually for each person. This is only about one-fifth the level in middle- and high-income developing countries.

Developing countries also lack professional staff. Among the sixty-five countries surveyed, the number of professional staff engaged in agricultural research (about 23 000) is hardly more than the number that exists in Japan alone. National agricultural research systems in many developing countries also lack strong problem-solving, development-oriented research institutions, and sound policies to foster the development of agricultural technology. The commitment to implement such policies also is frequently wanting (Wortman and Cummings, 1978, p. 129). Moreover, after 1970, international financial support to the national research systems declined (Evenson, 1977, p. 238), which added to their already existing problems.

THE INTERNATIONAL RESEARCH SYSTEM

Clearly, the developing countries need help in conducting agricultural research, and they might best receive it from international no-strings-attached research centers situated in the Third World itself (George, 1976, p. 282). This conclusion was the basis for the establishment of an international agricultural research system. The Rockefeller Foundation, having already succeeded in co-operation with the government of Mexico in the sponsorship of research adapting high-yielding wheats, teamed up with the Ford Foundation to establish the International Rice Research Institute (IRRI) in the Philippines in 1960, with the co-operation of the host government. The IRRI was the first unit in what has now become an international system of agricultural research institutes. The founding of the International Rice Research Institute was the institutional embodiment of the conviction that high-quality agricultural research and its technological extensions would increase rice production, ease the food supply situation, speed commercial prosperity in the rural areas, and defuse agrarian radicalism (Anderson *et al.*, 1982, p. 7).

Significant international support for these and other international institutions began in 1972 through the newly established Consultative Group on International Agricultural Research (CGIAR), a multilateral forum of donors. The CGIAR system expanded rapidly during the 1970s, from $12 million being channeled to four institutes in 1971 to over $120 million in 1980 (Ruttan, 1982) to support thirteen International Agricultural Research Centers (IARCs), with some eight hundred scientists working in a wide range of disciplines (Oram, 1982, p. 392). In addition to its co-sponsors, the CGIAR system is supported by thirty donors, including twenty national governments from both developed and developing countries plus a number of private foundations. This research system, although still quite new, now covers most of the major crops and animals, and extends to most areas of the developing countries.

The international institutes work on difficult problems of regional or international importance. They make germplasm freely available to co-operating countries, provide scientists to work co-operatively in national programs, hold meetings to review programs and exchange information, and train national scientists. The international institutes constitute one of the more successful modern-day examples of international co-operation. There is no doubt that the IARCs are playing a vital role in checking world hunger. As pointed out by Ruttan (1982, p. 132), 'The world will continue to need a system of international institutes that will play a strategic role in the areas of crop and livestock improvement'.

COMPARING THE US AND INTERNATIONAL SYSTEMS

Just as the advances and applications of science and technology have changed social structures within nations, they have also changed the international scene in a way that is substantial and accelerating. The agricultural system in the US has encouraged the changes in international areas such as growing interdependencies among nations, new patterns of resource use, and the development of technology that is global in nature. Some of the developments in agricultural research which affect international relations are rather subtle: increased pressure to establish capabilities for dealing with hunger, substantial changes in the agricultural policy of national governments, and the growth of what has been referred to by Skolnikoff (1977, p. 507) as transnational relationships (international relationships outside governments).

Since its inception, and particularly since the end of the Second World War, the US model of agricultural research has been actively diffused throughout the world. Japan, India, Brazil and other smaller nations have based significant portions of their research system upon the US model. Agricultural scientists and research administrators have frequently traversed the less industrialized nations in an effort to convince the leaders of those countries of the wisdom of adopting the US model for organizing agricultural research (Busch and Lacy, 1983, p. 2).

In spite of the awareness that it is in the national interest to deal with questions of international poverty, malnutrition and low productivity because those problems are tied to US economic and security interests (Koppel, 1981), agricultural research policy studies have seldom reflected the issues of international concern for agricultural research. Most national and international systems have been studied in isolation without due consideration of the international relations and framework within which the agricultural research systems operate. Most of the studies have reflected local, state or national perspectives.

The reasons for this are logical and stem from several factors. Historically, science and technology have been seen by governments as a means of serving national or local interests. They developed from within particular social and political settings, and there are inherently greater opportunities for productive research within a national setting. Unfortunately, this basically national research orientation has some undesirable effects: lack of anticipation and understanding of the international changes brought by science and technology, and an inability to cope adequately with issues as they impinge on international affairs (Skolnikoff, 1977, p. 508).

There have been a few attempts to examine the formal linking of the US land-grant system and the international agricultural research system (e.g. Koppel, 1981). Koppel observes that the international functions of the land-grant system include: educating significant numbers of foreign students in the US; conducting research which is directly transferable to developing countries; directly strengthening foreign agricultural research and extension systems; and appraising, implementing and evaluating international agricultural development projects. This linkage is particularly emphasized by Busch and Lacy (1983, p. 238). They note that 'this linkage is particularly important in the light of the development of a significant number of new approaches to agricultural research in other nations'. Given the momentum of the existing organization of the agricultural policy field, such overall studies for the most part are rather general, with limited objectives for any policy issue or research interest.

Appropriateness of the model

To some extent, the international agricultural research institutes are modeled on the land-grant system in the United States (Busch and Sachs, 1981, p. 146). The replication of this model involved the transfer, not only of specific cultural practices and biomedical and mechanical innovations, but also of entire institutions and the value system associated with them. Both the IARC and the land-grant systems have tended to utilize scientific knowledge to transform agriculture into a more productive system. The package of goods that has been introduced by the international institutes is essentially the same as that which has been developed in the United States, except that the international institutes are more crop-specific than the land-grant system (Busch and Sachs, 1981, p. 146).

However, the systems differ on some philosophical issues. The American agricultural research system set out to transform American agriculture into a business and science with the emphasis on efficiency. For most of the beneficiaries of international systems, agriculture remains a way of life and of subsistence, and not a capitalistic enterprise. Secondly, the American system encouraged mechanization in farming, whereas the international system has to work for social systems where agriculture continues to be based upon manual and bullock power.

It has been argued that the transfer of an entire model of experiment stations from one society to another where the fundamental features of rural life and work, of society and politics are wholly different, constituted an inappropriate form of technology transfer (Brass, 1982, p. 105).

Some thinkers have even expressed the fear that the US research system, characterized by a highly developed institutional infrastructure linking universities to other private and public institutions involved in technical, social and economic change, rarely performs as an effective instrument of technical, social and cultural change when transported into societies where the presumed institutional infrastructure does not exist (Ruttan, 1982, p. 123). But the excellent results achieved by the international institutes in the transformation of agriculture in many areas of the world may have demonstrated the soundness, efficacy and relevance of the pattern of the American agricultural research system for agricultural research systems which operate on a different resource base and level of development. From this essential consonance, a research partnership has evolved between American agricultural research systems and the international agricultural research systems. This partnership has become a major force in the worldwide process of the commercialization and modernization of agriculture, transforming the quality of life and the relationship of men and women to the land in most of the less industrialized countries.

Comparing funding systems

The US land-grant system is supported by two research funding mechanisms. First, the institutional research support system provides funds to support the research program of a particular research institution. The selection of the research program is developed by the administration and staff of the experiment station or research institute. Second, the project research grant system provides support through project grants to individual scientists or research teams. In this system, allocation of research effort is typically determined by the granting agency, be it state or federal government, foundation, corporation or commodity group.

The international agricultural research system is supported mainly by the institutional research mechanism. The funds from donor countries and organizations are channeled through the CGIAR. The Consultative Group provides a forum in which international institutes set forth their program and funding needs and the donors make known their funding commitments. The commitments of the individual donors are typically made to a particular institute rather than the system as a whole.

Comparing returns to investment

The major share of the growth of agricultural productivity in the US has taken place since the mid-1930s. Indeed, agricultural productivity growth did not begin until forty years after the establishment of agricultural experiment stations in the 1880s (Peterson and Fitzharris, 1977, p. 74). The possible explanation for this long, dry spell is that agricultural research simply did not produce any significant results during its early years. However, Peterson and Fitzharris argue that the bulk of the research input before 1925 was necessary simply to maintain productivity. The long-term growth in agricultural productivity began in 1937. For the first six-year period (1937–42) the internal rate of return to investment in research was 50 per cent. The rate of return to research investment in the periods 1957–62 and 1967–72 was 49 per cent and 34 per cent respectively (Peterson and Fitzharris, 1977, p. 78). The predicted marginal internal rate of return for 1971–76 was 29 per cent. From this trend it can be observed that over a period of time the return to investment in agricultural research in the US has declined considerably.

On the other hand, the internal rate of return on investment by the International Rice Research Institute in the first fifteen years is estimated to be about 80 per cent (World Bank, 1981). Roughly speaking, similar returns have been estimated in rice research by the International Center for Tropical Agriculture (CIAT). Dalrymple (1977) has not carried through to the point of calculating the actual cost-benefit ratio, but he suggests that the returns to international research in wheat and rice must have been very high. One result of the very high rates of return to the initial investment in IRRI, CIMMYT and CIAT has been to create high expectations for the other international institutes.

DEVELOPMENT OF POLITICAL SUPPORT

One of the interacting roles of US and international agricultural research systems is in developing support for the research endeavor. Support may be defined broadly as the means to existence and sustenance within the environment. Support involves 'legitimacy', which means acceptance and approval from those who share and control the environment. Legitimacy is an underlying condition for providing material resources or funding required to maintain and advance the research institutions.

Maintaining legitimacy

US public agricultural research has been regarded for more than a century as a legitimate function of state and national governments. However, there have been occasional challenges to the belief, which underlies acceptance, that agricultural progress is obtained through improved technology. These challenges include the nineteenth-century anti-science movements, and the nineteenth-century populists who preferred social to technological solutions for maintaining prosperous family farms.

In recent years, as William Browne points out in Chapter 6, groups have raised concerns that new agricultural technology was being developed regardless of its effects upon natural resources and the natural environment, although some of these concerns have since been addressed by research and regulatory agencies.

Concerns about impacts of technology upon farming structure have been more enduring because US agricultural research clearly did facilitate, though it did not dictate, increased size and fewer farming units. In developing countries, rapid off-farm migration has resulted in some economic dependency and political instability, but there can be no easy judgment on the costs and benefits of agricultural change in these countries. Outmigration results from increased human fertility and survival as well as from labor-saving technology, and this technology may also increase productivity needed for feeding the larger populations. Under pressure of population growth, technology change seems inevitable.

It can be argued on behalf of the IARCs that, because their emphasis is upon improving genetic materials, the new technology which they produce is scale neutral and has aided small farm agriculture. Scientists surveyed at the international centers believed that small farmers are the principal beneficiaries of their research and publications (Gajbhiye and Hadwiger, 1986).

Along with distributing technology benefits more broadly among producers, the international centers have been crucial in distributing productive capacity. Thanks to the centers' work in improving the genetic capability of rice, wheat and other food grains, India, China and other populous nations are becoming self-sufficient in food, allaying fears that modern technology would direct agricultural resources to the production of expensive luxury foods. The work of international centers, having increased productivity and also having distributed benefits widely, has enhanced the legitimacy of public agricultural research.

Achieving material support

Legitimacy is but one level of support for agricultural research. With legitimacy it becomes possible to move to a second level – providing the material resources needed to maintain the various research establishments. Several motives may be identified for providing such resources – motives common to governments, non-profit foundations or private entities.

First, legitimacy itself may lead to support 'in the public interest'. Agricultural research has always had 'public interest' advocates who would not personally benefit from research outcomes. Supporters during the nineteenth century were likely to be utopians who envisioned a future of abundance and leisure brought about by technological development (Hadwiger, 1984, pp. 194–5). Such a pay-off is now being realized, and so it is not surprising that private foundations which seek the public interest should have provided leadership and generous support in the development of the international research centers. For institutions and individuals who contribute to such a public interest goal there are the side benefits of public recognition and acclaim. In the US Congress, for example, influential legislators seeking a fitting memorial to their own years of service have sometimes dictated new budget lines for agricultural research. Such assistance based on philanthropic impulse has produced substantial increments in relatively small budgets, such as those for agricultural research.

A second basis of material support is client interest. Among the beneficiaries and potential clients of agricultural research are the producers and/or consumers of food and fiber – a rather large constituency. Consumers, unfortunately, have not been well mobilized as specific clientèles, though they are considered to be the largest research beneficiaries (Hildreth, 1982, p. 241). Among the explanations offered for this anomaly are: (a) consumer benefits are diffuse rather than exclusive, so it pays no consumer to advocate for himself/herself; (b) research institutions cater to producers as their major clients, so when consumer groups perceive that benefits to them were unintended, they become defensive rather than supportive. But for consumer organizations these should not be insuperable problems. These groups presumably do seek the interests of all consumers, and their staffs are capable of perceiving and supporting both indirect and direct benefits. Similarly, governmental budget and planning agencies, which also seek consumer goals such as avoiding inflation and reducing poverty, should be able to perceive and support the benefits of agricultural research.

There are difficulties also in mobilizing producer groups, but these have usually been overcome. Among these difficulties are: (a) producers who support public research must accept that the technology which is generated may benefit other producers who did not support the research; and (b) improvements from technology benefits tend to be passed on to consumers through improved products and lower prices. Strategies have been devised to overcome these problems. First, much producer support is decentralized, as Alan Marcus points out in Chapter 2, in order to maximize exclusive benefits to supporters. Producer groups attach themselves to a particular research institution or group, in the expectation that it will be responsive to their unique geographic or commodity needs. Such producers benefit as first users of this specific new knowledge, and, as a trade-off, they accept the likelihood that some knowledge may later be adapted to the needs of other producers.

Of course, producers have sometimes tried to slow this process of dissemination. For example, US producers have generally refused to support efforts to adapt US technology for developing country producers. Earlier they opposed the use of US agricultural attachés to promote agricultural development and reform abroad. Currently any international agricultural research sponsored by the USDA must meet criteria that assure that it mainly serves US producers (Joint Council on Food and Agricultural Sciences, 1984, p. 323). The US government nevertheless provides agricultural technical assistance to developing countries through budgets other than the USDA's, including a sizeable contribution to the International Agricultural Research Centers.

It can be argued that US producers should support this international research, along with the research that serves their particular needs. While conceding that the dissemination of technology has increased world production, contributing to the once-depressing carry-overs of recent years, one should not leap to the conclusion that producers will suffer from further technology advances. First, it may be argued that the current abundance cannot be sustained without new technology. Economist Ken Farrell has predicted that further technology advance is needed to meet future demands:

> To meet projected needs for 2020 without additional productivity enhancing technology and improved production systems would place inordinate pressure on the nation's natural resource base and induce serious environmental consequences and very likely could be achieved only at substantial increases in real consumer prices for food, fiber, and forest products (Joint Council on Food and Agricultural Sciences, 1984, p. 76).

It can also be argued that when a commodity becomes widely adapted, all producers of that commodity benefit. New uses may accompany new production, as, for example, when producers in a new locality stimulate local demand greater than they themselves can supply. In a real sense, producers of a commodity often compete less with each other than with producers of alternative foods, because diets are increasingly flexible (Hadwiger, 1982), and because governments seeking self-sufficiency are protecting producers from foreign competition but not from consumer shifts to other domestically produced foods.

So among producers of a specific commodity there is often a complementarity of interest in research which would improve the commodity *vis-à-vis* other products, e.g. make it more resilient in the environment, more convenient in handling and storage, and more attractive to consumers. Rice, for example, because of increased yields, remains an able competitor to wheat among a large percentage of the world's population, and it should be remembered that these yield increases came mainly not from developed country research but from the International Rice Research Institute.

One can therefore construct a profile of political support for agricultural research, according to which the US agricultural system and also the international research centers would remain vital contributors, and whereby national institutions in developing countries would also assume a major role in the international research system. But one must begin by acknowledging that major beneficiaries of research, such as consumers and small farmers, are difficult to mobilize as supporters. The major clientèle – producers in developed countries – do not support agricultural research in general but rather as particular sets of research activities. When confronted with the integrated and international character of the research establishment, these producers understandably have mixed feelings, although these groups no longer display the anxieties about international research which some revealed in the 1950s.

Support for research institutions from public interest organizations may continue to be forthcoming, based on achievements. Research institutions have increased food supplies, demonstrating the potential for meeting increasing world food needs. Efforts of the international research centers have shown the potentiality for technology to serve the small producers and poor consumers. The research institutions have good access to the decision-makers within governments and private funding agencies who are able to increase budgets for reasons of public interest. In effect, there may be a worldwide institutional lobby, with an attitude of mutuality, and a fairly large vision of the international research system.

Given that the research output will continue to be impressive, and that the cost will be small relative to other public budgets, it would seem that the prospects are good for a healthy and expanding international research system. Its future may be more promising than that of other international systems which have depended on legitimacy, such as the United Nations and its agencies.

CONCLUDING COMMENTS

The US agricultural system and the international research centers are complementary, on balance, in their efforts to develop support for their own missions. In particular, the IARCs, in exhibiting an ability to help small-unit farming, can reassure those who fear that new technology may not be beneficial to the world's smaller farmers. The combined achievements of the agricultural institutions provide a strong rationale for continuing support from public interest groups, eleemosynary foundations, and benevolent governments.

Support from producers has been channeled to separate research institutions rather than to the international research system because producers wanted to be first users of knowledge highly adapted to their specific needs. But there are now reasons for supporting research on an international basis. The international centers enhance the legitimacy of all agricultural research. And improvements in a commodity which make it more competitive with alternative foods may help all producers of that commodity.

Historically, as Alan Marcus notes in Chapter 2, leaders of the research establishment have persuaded producers that they benefit from research, and this is a continuing task. Meanwhile, agricultural research institutions should also tout their capabilities to the large constituency of consumer interests. They can explain that new technology has contributed remarkably to the goal of adequate low-cost food, and further that national and international technology has been disseminated and legitimized through interaction between national and international research institutions.

Note

1. Funding for this project was provided by the World Food Institute, Iowa State University, Ames, Iowa. We would like to thank Charlette Roderick, Director, World Food Institute; Dr Charles L. Mulford, Professor, Sociology, ISU; and Dr Gerald Klonglan, Chair, Dept of Sociology and Anthropology, for their encouragement and guidance.

References

Anderson, R. S., Brass, P. R., Levy, E. and Morrison, B. M. (1982) *Science, Politics and the Agricultural Revolution in Asia* (Boulder, Colorado: Westview Press).

Brass, P. R. (1982) 'Institutional Transfer of Technology: The Land-Grant Model and the Agricultural University at Pantnagar', in Anderson, P. R., Levy, E. and Morrison, B. M. (eds) *Science, Politics and the Agricultural Revolution in Asia* (Boulder, Colorado: Westview Press).

Busch, L. and Lacy, W. B. (1983) *Science, Agriculture and the Politics of Research* (Boulder, Colorado: Westview Press).

Busch, L. and Sachs, C. (1981) 'The Agricultural Sciences and the Modern World System', in Busch, L. (ed.) *Science and Agricultural Development* (Totowa, New Jersey: Allanheld, Osmun).

Dalrymple, D. G. (1977) 'Evaluating the Impact of International Research on Wheat and Rice Production in the Developing Nations', in Arndt, T. M., Dalrymple, D. G. and Ruttan, V. W. (eds) *Resource Allocation and Productivity in National and International Agricultural Research* (Minneapolis: University of Minnesota Press).

Evenson, R. E. (1977) 'Comparative Evidence on Returns to Investment in National and International Research Institutions', in Arndt, T. M., Dalrymple, D. G. and Ruttan, V. W. (eds) *Resource Allocation and Productivity in National and International Agricultural Research* (Minneapolis: University of Minnesota Press).

Gajbhiye, H. and Hadwiger, D. F. (1986) 'The International Role of the US Agricultural Research System: Perspectives from a Comparison of US and International Work Settings', in Busch, L. and Lacey, W. (eds)

The Agricultural Scientific Enterprise: a system in tradition (Boulder, Colorado: Westview Press).
George, S. (1976) *How the Other Half Dies* (Montclair: Allanheld, Osmun).
Hadwiger, D. F. (1982) 'Nutrition, Food Safety, and Farm Policy', in Hadwiger, D. F. and Talbot, R. B. (eds) *Food Policy and Farm Programs* (New York: The Academy of Political Science).
Hadwiger, D. F. (1984) 'US Agricultural Research Politics: Utopians, Utilitarians, Copians', in *Food Policy*, 9: 193–205.
Hildreth, R. J. (1982) 'The Agricultural Research Establishment in Transition', in Hadwiger, D. F. and Talbot, R. B. (eds) *Food Policy and Farm Programs* (New York: The Academy of Political Science).
Joint Council on Food and Agricultural Sciences (1984) *Reference Document: Needs Assessment for the Food and Agricultural Sciences.*
Koppel, B. (1981) *Report of a Workshop on Linkages Between the International and Domestic Functions of the Land-Grant System* (Honolulu: East-West Center).
Oram, P. (1982) 'Collaboration of National and International Institutions', in Anderson, R. S., Brass, P. R., Levy, E. and Morrison, B. M. (eds) *Science, Politics and the Agricultural Revolution in Asia* (Boulder, Colorado: Westview Press).
Peterson, W. L. and Fitzharris, J. C. (1977) 'Organization and Productivity of the Federal-State Research System in the United States', in Arndt, T. M., Dalrymple, D. G. and Ruttan, V. W. (eds) *Resource Allocation and Productivity* (Minneapolis: University of Minnesota Press).
Ruttan, V. W. (1982) *Agricultural Research Policy* (Minneapolis: University of Minnesota Press).
Skolnikoff, E. B. (1977) 'Science, Technology and the International System', in Spiegal-Rosing, I. and Price, D. de Sollar (eds) *Science, Technology and Society* (Beverly Hills, California: Sage).
World Bank (1981) *Agricultural Research: Sector Policy Paper* (Washington, DC: World Bank).
Wortman, S. and Cummings, R. W. Jr (1978) *To Feed This World* (Baltimore: Johns Hopkins University Press).

6 An Emerging Opposition? Agricultural Interests and Federal Research Policy

William P. Browne

Studies that link agricultural policy and interest group politics generally focus on the supportive aspects of lobbying. Observers as diverse in viewpoint and background as Theodore Lowi (1979) and Charles Hardin (1978) contend that agricultural insiders from Congress, administrative bureaus, and interest groups set policy by bringing an agreed-upon consensus to centralized points of decision-making. Within the agricultural establishment, highly centralized clusters or networks of participants are seen as developing their own agreements in a fragmented and decentralized political universe (Meyer and Dishman, undated). The key elements that are seen to be maintaining these well-ordered arrangements include the ability of all participants to compromise within their own decisional networks, reciprocity between networks, and trust in the judgements of policymaking colleagues. In short, governing networks work because no one destroys the legitimacy and expertise of the principal players.

Recent studies of interest groups, however, observe an extensive proliferation of organized groups (Walker, 1983). This proliferation may be of policy consequence in that the expansion of interests brings more narrow and diverse representation, policy opinions, ideological views, and, accordingly, claims about program needs. Gais, Peterson and Walker (1984) conclude that this expansion of interests makes compromise difficult and destabilizes the policy process. So many competing voices, when increasingly heard in an environment where recipricol agreements are prized, add only confusion for policymakers as they seek to agree upon specific program content and funding.

In the policy arena of agricultural research, previous studies agree with the important role played by supportive interest groups (McCalla, 1978; Hadwiger, 1982). However, Harold Guither (1980) has detailed a rapidly expanding number of agricultural interests, and Don Hadwiger (1982, pp. 150–68) has analyzed the emerging impact of some of these on research policy. Is an organized opposition to research policy emerging from among these proliferating interests?

What are the concerns of opposing interests and who do they represent? This paper seeks to expand on the Hadwiger research by briefly examining the array of interests and arguments critical of agricultural research policy in the 1980s.

THE STUDY AND ITS METHODS

Criticisms of agricultural research range from mundane to serious, from inflammatory in intent to specific proposals for policy change. This analysis is concerned only with those complaints that might have potential consequences for future agricultural research funding and programs. As a result, the research presented here examined (a) all organized interests who claimed to speak as representatives of some facet of American agriculture, (b) their negative public comments to the mass media or through media releases, and (c) their placing of such remarks in the context of reform-oriented agricultural legislation of the early to mid-1980s. It was understood from previous studies of lobbying (Milbrath, 1963; Zeigler and Baer, 1968) that these remarks would vary in purpose from statements of actual and immediate legislative goals to those intended to raise questions and doubts in the minds of others as to long-term policy needs. Some claims, it was known, would accurately reflect the perceptions of the interests involved, while others would be purposely exaggerated in order to maximize attention and coverage. Still other remarks would be made as bargaining proposals, later to be discarded by their proponents in return for other policy considerations. Previous studies (Truman, 1951; Milbrath, 1963; Wilson, 1973) also made it clear that the remarks of some interests were of generally greater consequence than those of others, since lobbies were not equal in their legitimacy as policy spokespersons, their credibility among policy-makers, their reputations as knowledgeable observers, or in other resources for effectively pursuing legislative change.

The intent of this analysis was to predict neither the sequence nor likelihood of change. The policy environment in which so many participants have potential influence makes it unlikely that interest groups can independently control the direction of legislation. Nor can interests isolate, singularly nurture, or monopolize the use by others of a policy-relevant idea generated by their initial critiques. This article undertakes the more modest but far more useful task of compiling a typology of interest group-based critiques of agricultural research policy. It then makes note of the type of agriculturally concerned interests voicing these complaints and, finally, offers some observations about the place these critical interests occupy in agricultural policy-making.[1] The latter allow the reader to make some judgements about the potential consequences of these attacks on agricultural research.

The data used here were compiled as part of a larger study of the relationships between agricultural policy and interest group politics.[2] That study, at its onset, identified 215 interests taking positions on federal agricultural legislation from 1980 to 1985. Nearly a third of these interests were found to take some stance on agricultural research issues.

TAKING POLICY POSITIONS

When research policy is addressed by agricultural interests, remarks are generally supportive, but usually brief. Organizations such as the National Grange are most typical in their attention. They label research as a positive good, note it to be a cornerstone of American agriculture, and go on to address more pressing matters of farm life and economics in greater detail. A few other groups are left to address the specific benefits of research and technology. The American Farm Bureau Federation, with its history of broad support for research (Hadwiger, 1982, pp. 92–3), continues to list several projects and problems as important legislative matters. A number of larger commodity organizations, such as the National Corn Growers Association, target specific areas of research need and lobby on behalf of particular research centers. But both the AFBF and the commodity interests have far more extensive concerns which consume their lobbyists' time and attention than agricultural research. This means that the most extensive and detailed statements of support come from those interests that are some part of the research effort. These include, among others, the National Association of State Universities and Land-Grant Colleges, the Agriculture Research Institute, the National 4-H Council, and the American Veterinary Medical Association. Looking at these supportive groups as a whole, one can conclude that agricultural research tells its own story and counts many friendly allied groups.

Nonetheless, there are other claims being made. Five types of complaints are often repeated. These address questions of costs, program beneficiaries, product quality and safety, environmental use, and control of the research agenda.

COSTS

As the costs of farm support programs increased during the 1980s and as concerns over federal budget deficits heightened, a variety of traditional farm interests began asking whether too much of the total agricultural budget goes to research and research institutions. This set of comments became especially evident as planning for the 1985 Farm Bill took place. Most congressional and administration sources, at the time, were indicating that agriculture would suffer some cuts; and, apparently, some farm interests see research programs as a lower priority than direct farm assistance. Both general farm and commodity groups have joined with many of the protest-style farm coalitions in making these demands. The most pointed and direct cost-related questions are about the research institutions. Some farm groups point out that the colleges of agriculture and research stations should, in principle, share equally with producers in existing financial hard times. Others, including the National Farmers' Union and the protest groups such as the American Agriculture Movement, argue that research institutions do too little for farmers and deserve stringent cuts. These groups see much of the research funding going toward institutional maintenance and support rather than into useful commodity or conservation services.

PROGRAM BENEFICIARIES

Those who question research costs, as just noted, are often criticizing programs on the basis of those who are perceived to be the primary beneficiaries. Farm activists with experience in land-grant settings frequently charge that the main beneficiaries of funding are university administrators and researchers with esoteric programs. Groups concerned with rural development, such as Rural America, and consumer interests make similar complaints.

Rural and consumer public interest style groups, along with numerous farm protest organizations, also level charges that research funds selectively reward large-scale producers while neglecting smaller ones. Often these complaints are couched in the rhetoric of family versus corporate farm, with research institutions portrayed as the allies of large, multi-faceted corporations. These agricultural spokespersons often note the linkages between research, mechanization and large-scale farming while pointing out that the current financial plight of many farm families is due to purchases of land and equipment, undertaken to achieve the same economies of scale that agricultural research already provided for the nation's largest producers.

PRODUCT QUALITY AND SAFETY

Two very different sets of complaints are made about the inferiority of many of today's farm products in comparison with those of the past. Organizations of consumers, alternative agriculturalists and rural environmentalists challenge the nutritional quality of current food as well as the safety to the consumer of chemical soil applications and animal medications. Research scientists and institutions are held responsible for developing new genetic strains and farming techniques with regard only for ease of harvesting and transportation. Animal rights organizations concur with these complaints, expressing their discontent with rearing arrangements and feedlot conditions.

The second set of complaints is made by major agribusiness interests rather than by groups on the fringes of agriculture. Their concerns are over consumer resistance to hard fruits, tasteless vegetables, and oddly textured meats. A number of specialized commodity groups, trade associations and food retail representatives express the belief that inadequate attention to consumer tastes by agricultural scientists threatens them with losses as buyers move to more palatable products. Increased seafood consumption and the rise of large numbers of specialized food markets are cited as evidence. While such interests acknowledge that existing products may have marketing benefits in being less seasonally restricted, available in larger quantities, and more transportable, some of these groups nonetheless claim that scientists held accountable for sales would have concerned themselves more with product desirability than have agricultural scientists funded through federal appropriations.

ENVIRONMENTAL USE

Closely related to issues of product quality in terms of both concerns and interests voicing them are some issues of environmental use. Criticisms of the role played by research institutions in promoting fertilizers, pesticides, herbicides and such chemical-intensive farming methods as no-till agriculture are frequently raised. The impact of modern agriculture on both soil and water is questioned by, primarily, organizations of non-farmers and non-market interests.

Environmental criticisms do not come only from public interest groups of consumers and conservationists. Many people are worried that agricultural research does nothing to assist (d) compatibility between farm and recreation or farm and commercial users of rural areas, (b) the utilization of indigenous labor and resources, (c) the stabilization and development of rural communities, and (d) local governments and utilities in providing economical and efficient services for all rural residents. While such complaints are most frequently voiced by rural interests with little standing in agricultural policy networks, those groups, such as the Catholic Rural Life Conference and the Rural Coalition, are frequently in contact with associations of local government, manufacturing and tourist industries. In addition, several forestry associations voice related criticisms from inside the agriculture establishment.

CONTROL OF THE RESEARCH AGENDA

The final set of criticisms of agricultural research may be among the most recently emerging. Don Hadwiger (1982, pp. 90–114) found, for the most part, support for agricultural research from those who directly benefited from its activities, including trade groups whose private developmental research flowed from that undertaken in public institutions. To some extent, this compatibility is being lost.

Many private firms have moved into the area of biotechnology. These seek federal support directly, often outside of agriculture, and see some activities of agricultural scientists as unfair competition. Other long-standing participants in agricultural research endeavors have become critical of various aspects of the performances of past partners. Things go so slowly. Too many side issues of social, economic and environmental concern cloud their work. There are too few opportunities to direct new investigations or modify existing studies.

Agricultural researchers are 'unresponsive'. As a result, these associations and firms would like to examine the prospects of new forms of co-operative ventures or work toward new relationships with state and national research institutions.

In a sense, however, the complaints of those who seek to make a financial profit from technological breakthroughs in agriculture are little different from those of other interests with complaints about present research policy. That is to say, as private interests, these groups are unable to direct federal programs as they want in order to meet their own specific goals. As a result, a variety of interests have found some reason from their diverse perspectives, to argue against what they see as the prevailing patterns of influence in agricultural research.

THE IMPLICATIONS

Policy positions critical of agricultural research are surprisingly extensive and broad-based in the 1980s. Critics represent a cross-section of interests involved in agricultural policy-making. It must be concluded that a large number of interests have become discontented with many of the results of agricultural research as developed from a supportive policy network. The policy process, relative to position-taking on research issues, is the destabilized environment of conflicting interests described by Gais, Peterson and Walker (1984) rather than an environment of reciprocating decisional networks.

Critical interests include (a) the array of farm protest groups that have formed in the late 1970s and 1980s in response to the depressed farm economy, (b) several traditional farm organizations, including both those who have supported and those who have questioned research policy in the past, (c) a number of market-oriented firms and associations with no history of substantial disagreement with research policy, and (d) a lengthy list of organizations that have been only marginally active in agricultural policy-making. These interests have considerable potential for influence. The established farm interests occupy their own legitimate positions in national policy-making (Browne, 1982). Agribusiness firms and associations employ a wide range of competent and frequently well-known Washington-based lobbyists (Salisbury, 1983). The protest groups have proven effective in gaining considerable media attention, which in turn attracts political decision-makers (Browne, 1983). Environmental, consumer and rural development groups have their own supporters both among the public and in Congress; and these interests have successfully worked in coalition arrangements with other influential groups in the past (Berry, 1982).

But, while broad ranging, there is not evidence that these critics are allied against agricultural research policy. On the contrary, their demands vary widely and frequently run counter to one another. To redesign the direction of agricultural research for any one of these interests would cause even greater dissatisfaction among the others. For example, greater restrictions on chemical use would hardly benefit private firms who want to market more abundant and inexpensive products. Coalition arrangements among the critics, while perhaps most feasible for smaller-scale producers and the public interest style organizations, would entail such extensive compromises that any alliances would be difficult to maintain and likely to be shortlived. As a result, it appears unlikely that leadership from any of these lobbies will produce new directions in agricultural research. Thus, present criticisms may prove to have little consequence for research policy.

The inability of these groups to influence policy changes does not preclude them from having an impact, however. The active presence of so many competing demands on research policy could have two potentially negative effects, both owing to what Gais, Peterson and Walker (1984) refer to as instability in the policy process. First, agricultural research policy might eventually be determined in such a way as to divide up and allocate projects and programs among an even greater number of targeted clientèle. In this way, many of the critics would gain their own selective form of benefits (Olson, 1965, p. 51) from agricultural research. Given present policy concerns which conspicuously divide funds among regions and producer types, this scenario is not unlikely. Because total research funding is not likely to expand, such redistributive action would have a restrictive impact on present research efforts.

The second effect that policy instability could produce would be even more financially restrictive to agricultural research. It may well be that the plethora of critical voices diminishes both the credibility of agricultural researchers and the ability of their political supporters effectively to gain support for research efforts. As a consequence, as budgetary deficit and funding concerns become intensive, policy-makers might well apply the largest and most burdensome cuts to what they see as controversial programs.

For those concerned with agricultural research policy, the lesson to be learned from this criticism is at once clear-cut and yet uncertain. Quite obviously, researchers should be aware of those who have been antagonized by their efforts and should look for the reasons for this discontent. Those in charge of research policy must be prepared to answer the critics in order to minimize misinformation and its potentially destabilizing results. Uncertainty, however, comes about in terms of whether or not these criticisms will or will not matter to policy-makers. The only answer that can be given is that sometimes organized interests do make a political difference and sometimes they do not. As noted above, the potential exists each way. The eventual outcome for agricultural research depends on who listens to both supporters and critics and what these listeners do about what they hear.

Notes

1. These were collected from the daily clippings file (1980–5) maintained by the Economic Research Service, United States Department of Agriculture and from organizational newsletters and releases.
2. That study was supported by joint funding from the Central Michigan University and the Farm and Rural Economy Branch, Economic Research Service, United States Department of Agriculture.

References

Browne, William P. (1982) 'Farm Organizations and Agribusiness', in Don F. Hadwiger and Ross B. Talbot (eds) *Food Policy and Farm Programs* (New York: The Academy of Political Science): 198–211.

Browne, William P. (1983) 'Mobilizing and Activating Group Demands: The American Agriculture Movement', *Social Science Quarterly*, 64 (March): 19–34.

Berry, Jeffrey M. (1982) 'Consumers and the Hunger Lobby', in Don F. Hadwiger and Ross B. Talbot (eds) *Food Policy and Farm Programs* (New York: Academy of Political Science): 68–78.

Gais, Thomas L., Peterson, Mark A. and Walker, Jack L. (1984) 'Interest Groups, Iron Triangles and Representative Institutions in American National Government', *British Journal of Political Science*, 14 (April): 161–85.

Guither, Harold D. (1980) *The Food Lobbyists* (Lexington, Mass.: Lexington Books).

Hadwiger, Don F. (1982) *The Politics of Agricultural Research* (Lincoln: University of Nebraska Press).

Hardin, Charles M. (1978) 'Agricultural Price Policy: The Political Role of Bureaucracy', in Don F. Hadwiger and William P. Browne (eds) *The New*

Politics of Food (Lexington, Mass.: Lexington Books): 7–13.
Lowi, Theodore J. (1979) *The End of Liberalism*, second edition (New York: W. W. Norton).
McCalla, Alex F. (1978) 'Politics of the Agricultural Research Establishment', in Don F. Hadwiger and William P. Browne (eds) *The New Politics of Food* (Lexington, Mass.: Lexington Books): 77–91.
Meyer, Neil L. and Dishman, William T. (undated) *Power Clusters: How Public Policy Originates* (Moscow: University of Idaho).
Milbrath, Lester W. (1963) *The Washington Lobbyists* (Chicago: Rand McNally).
Olson, Mancur (1965) *The Logic of Collective Action* (Cambridge, Mass.: Harvard University Press).
Salisbury, Robert H. (1984) 'Interest Representation: The Dominance of Institutions', *American Political Science Review*, 78 (March): 64–76.
Truman, David B. (1951) *The Governmental Process* (New York: Alfred A. Knopf).
Walker, Jack L. (1983) 'The Origins and Maintenance of Interest Groups in America', *American Political Science Review*, 77 (June): 390–406.
Wilson, James Q. (1973) *Political Organizations* (New York: Basic Books).
Zeigler, L. Harmon and Baer, Michael A. (1968) *Lobbying: Interaction and Influence in State and Local Politics* (Belmont, Ca.: Wadsworth Publishing).

Part IV

The Prospects for Agenda Change

7 Toward a New Covenant for Agricultural Academe

J. Patrick Madden

In his book, *The Next Economy*, Paul Hawken (1983) has envisioned the US economy as it is likely to emerge from the current financial crisis, and the decline of the 'mass economy', or the economy of the industrial age. Agriculturalists ought to do a similar kind of thinking. We should ask ourselves what kind of agriculture is going to emerge from the current financial crisis, in which farm bankruptcies are becoming endemic, land prices and equipment values are plummeting, and the structure of agriculture is a blur. The past decade has seen unprecedented changes in US agriculture, and the rate of change seems to be accelerating. How will the land-grant institutions and other realms of academia adapt to The Next Agriculture? And more to the point, what will be our role in shaping the future of agriculture?

SUCCESS AS A MIXED BLESSING

American agriculture is heralded as a great success. Nurtured by scientific and educational systems, farmers not only make two or three blades of grass grow where none grew before, but they produce an abundance of food perhaps unprecedented in history. However, agricultural abundance has been both a blessing and a curse: food is plentiful for those who can afford it; prices are relatively low; and Americans spend a lower share of their income on food than any other industrial nation. Because some commodities have been supported above market-clearing prices, massive surpluses have been produced, causing a ruinous drain on the federal treasury. Farm mechanization has reduced the drudgery and risk of most farming operations (Splinter, 1980), while contributing to a loss of agricultural employment and the de-population of some farming areas and enriching other locations (Martin and Olmstead, 1985). Yield-enhancing fertilizers, pesticides and herbicides are heralded as an example of man's conquest over nature, while an increasing number of experts and consumer advocates have become alarmed about potential health hazards due to chemical residues appearing in ground water, streams and foods. Meanwhile, the increasingly prevalent exercises in setting national priorities for agricultural research and extension are frustrated by the absence of a clearly articulated set of national goals and an increasing number of vocal participants.

Interviews conducted during the Penn State study (Feller *et al.*, 1984, Vol. 2) illustrate the dedication of extension personnel to help farmers solve their various production problems. One of our interviewees, a prosperous Utah farmer, said he did not know how he would have survived had it not been for the help of the county extension agent and his staff. Then, upon further reflection, the farmer mused, 'On the other hand, if extension didn't do its job quite so well, maybe we wouldn't have all these burdensome surpluses'.

THE VOICES OF DISSENT

One interviewee likened the demise of millions of small family farms to the Holocaust. He contended that small farms are being exterminated through the overt actions of some extension personnel and the indifference of others.

I personally reject the charge that extension pretends to be the friend of the farmer while deviously jerking the rug out from under him, as inferred by some of the critics. The intentions are honorable. But sometimes the aggregate impact is the opposite of what was intended, as in the case of excess production suppressing prices in national and international markets.

Critics argue that the land-grant university system is not highly responsive to the needs of small- to moderate-scale family farms, and that adequate safeguards and guidelines do not exist for ensuring that judgements regarding negotiation of grants from private industry would remain within the institution's public interest. Researchers, according to some critics, tend to focus on increasing efficiency and production, rather than on attaining any structural ideal with regard to survival and prosperity of family farms. These critics view the primary clientèle of the land-grant agricultural research and extension system as wealthy farmers, agribusiness, chemical and machinery corporations, and other non-farm interests. These 'fat cats', according to this group of critics, are able to exert strong leverage on the mission and priorities of the system. By contributing a small amount of money to support research, they are able to persuade researchers and research administrators to alter the nature and scope of their research projects in a way that provides substantial in-kind contributions from the institutions to the firms in the form of non-reimbursed input of faculty time, laboratory or field research resources, and general overheads. Simultaneously, as a result of this kind of shift in emphasis, often little faculty time or research money remains to address the specific concerns of small- to moderate-scale family farms. Consequently, the wealthy interests are able to gain an even greater advantage over the already beleaguered small- to moderate-scale family farm (Strange, 1984). University officials and scientists respond that private grants are accepted only if they are compatible with established publicly supported research, and with the overall mission of the institution, which includes service to industries and to large as well as small farm operators. From this perspective, private grants are viewed as augmenting and quickening the research process.

Furthermore, critics allege that researchers develop a vested interest in ignoring the ecological impacts of toxic chemicals, and that no incentive exists within the system for researchers to find economically and environmentally sound methods of conserving and enhancing the productivity of the nation's natural and human resources. It is further contended that the motivation of private funding sources (principally the agribusiness corporations) is the hope that the research will enhance their after-tax net income. Little if any concern is focused on the ecological, community or humanitarian impacts of the manufacture or use of the technology resulting from such grants and contracts.

For example, a chemical company may give researchers a grant of a few thousand dollars, plus a supply of their chemical pesticide or herbicide to be tested under the field conditions found in that state. The researcher then would allocate certain experimental plots to the testing of this chemical for comparison with other competing chemicals and a control plot. Critics contend that the real beneficiaries of this research are the chemical companies, who can use the results of the university tests to advertise their products. Meanwhile, according to the critics, the chemical companies reap all the benefits while paying only a small fraction of the total cost of the research.

THE VIEW FROM WITHIN

Researchers interviewed had quite a different perspective. They agree that the chemical companies are not paying the full cost of evaluating their chemicals. But, the researchers contend, it costs proportionately little to add one more set of test plots to an experimental design. Furthermore, they say, it is essential for researchers to arrive at their own independent assessment of the effectiveness of the chemicals in different locations, as the basis for recommendations to farmers in their state. Critics would claim that it is inappropriate for publicly supported universities to perform contract testing of chemicals for private industry. Researchers respond by asking a rhetorical question: would it be better to have the fox guarding the chicken house? That is, would it be in the long-run interest of farmers and of society to have all the testing of chemicals done by private industry, rather than by scientists who subscribe to standards of objectivity and repeatability, and to peer review of methodology? The dialogue is at times shrill, and agreements are few.

Public debate regarding the optimum mix of scientific autonomy and social responsibility in publicly funded research organizations has intensified in recent years. For example, a public interest organization, California Rural Legal Assistance (CRLA), has brought suit against the University of California and that state's Cooperative Extension program, with charges that funds are being misappropriated and the fundamental mission of the land-grant system is betrayed in the choice of research objectives and extension methods. CRLA is demanding as relief that the University of California be required to delay initiation of publicly supported agricultural research until the potential social impacts have been studied and a committee of non-involved persons has approved the proposed research. Kendrick (1984, p. 1) has responded as follows:

> This allegation fails to recognize the nature of the benefit [of agricultural research] and its distribution among producer, supplier, and consumer.
>
> The social impact analysis of contemplated research called for by the plaintiffs would have a destructive impact on creativity and innovation in research. *All research*, whether in agriculture, engineering, physical science, medicine, the arts, humanities, or social sciences, *has potential positive and negative impacts* on societal values and structural configurations.

> The challenge to us as a people is not to stifle inquiry into the unknown, but to be wise enough to incorporate new knowledge into the fabric of living a better life within an organized society. Programs conducted by the Land-Grant Agricultural Experiment Stations and Cooperative Extension are undertaken on the assumption that an *enlightened society will accept or reject* findings and practices based on what it sees as being in its best interests.
>
> The broadest participation in the benefits from a technologically based agriculture in the United States accrues to the *consuming public*. The national interests of the United States are served by supporting, through research, extension, and other actions, the efficient production, processing, and marketing of the products of agriculture. (emphasis added)

In this statement, Kendrick is clearly emphasizing the impact of agricultural research on increasing consumer purchasing power through lower food prices. The contention that society will serve its own best interest by abundantly supporting agricultural research, with no 'social accounting' strings attached, seems to be based on three implicit value assumptions:

1. The 'greatest good for the greatest number of people' is assumed to be promoted by an ever-increasing abundance of agricultural commodities. Agricultural research that enables producers to increase production, productivity and efficiency are assumed inevitably to enhance the welfare of consumers through greater availability at lower prices.
2. It is assumed that if emerging technologies carry detrimental side-effects (pollution, social dislocation, unemployment, carcinogenic residues, etc.) then society will omnisciently anticipate severe side-effects.
3. It is further assumed that, in view of the anticipated impacts, an 'enlightened society', presumably including entrepreneurs and other decision-makers, will automatically reach a rational decision as to whether these disadvantages outweigh the advantages; that is, if the social disadvantages are expected to outweigh the anticipated advantages of adopting a technology, then that technology will be rejected. If, and only if, the social advantages are expected to prevail will the technology be adopted.

These assumptions have been subject to extensive criticism both from within and outside the agricultural academic establishment. For example, the axiom that more is better than less can be questioned in view of agricultural surpluses costing billions in federal funds. It is reasonable also to question whether the human condition is improved indefinitely with successively higher levels of consumption, at a time when obesity is a major threat to health. This incongruity does not imply, however, that efforts to increase agricultural productivity further should necessarily be terminated, but that a more holistic constellation of goals should be incorporated into the debate over the future of agriculture.

The second and third assumptions have also been severely questioned. Predictions of the harmlessness of chemicals and other technology have frequently been found to be incorrect years or even decades after widespread adoption. And the adoption of technology by private decision-makers is known to be affected more strongly by the promise of profit than by anticipated social and environmental impacts whose costs are not borne by the firm adopting the technology. Thus, the apparent assumptions underlying the argument for a *laissez-faire* approach to agricultural research are doubtful.

Among the most eloquent critics of the agricultural research system are some enlightened economists within the land-grant university system. For example, Bonnen (1983, p. 964) wrote:

> organizations, foundations, legal advocacy groups, and others . . . now constitute a Greek chorus of criticism of the performance of US agricultural institutions. Most cluster around the growing externalities of agricultural technology and public policy. These issues include environmental degradation; concerns for animal welfare, impacts on health and safety of farmers, agricultural workers, and consumers; adverse nutritional effects of production and processing technologies; the extrusion of smaller family farmers from agriculture, erosion of rural communities, and the concentration of agricultural production and economic wealth; adequate conservation and commercial exploitation of fragile lands that should not be in cultivation.
>
> *Focusing R&D investment on productivity and ever increasing growth* is not enough today. Equity, but also safety, quality of life, stability, and preservation of the environment for future generations, to name a few, must become major goals of agricultural R&D, as well as productivity and growth. In an urban society, soured on paying for malfunctioning farm programs to support farmers who are far wealthier than the typical taxpayer, these

> concerns must be dealt with or *agricultural scientists can expect to lose public support of agricultural R&D* . . . Greed is not a sufficient condition upon which to base public policy.
>
> Changes in society's values and social agenda, in part the consequence of externalities to agricultural policy and production, will remain an important source of disequilibria. This will require not only social science, physical and biological science, but also humanities research on the ethical and value conflicts in the choices that must be made. (emphasis added)

Various public interest organizations, highlighting possible links between agricultural research and the well-being of society, have called for conscious social planning. For example, Marty Strange (1984, p. 20) of the Nebraska-based Center for Rural Affairs has taken issue with the *laissez-faire* approach to agricultural research:

> There is a sort of feeling throughout the land that the unwanted is necessary. I simply can't accept that. I don't believe American agriculture has to unfold in any pre-determined way – we can have the kind of agriculture we want. That is, we can have the kind of agriculture we want within the limitations of nature, within the constraints established by the laws of nature – which constraints we've pretty well ignored in the last 100 years.

Castle (1981, p. 51) has noted: 'There seems to be an inability [of the land-grant/USDA system] to identify and then work with the major trends which are shaping our social environment'. During a conversation with the director of one of the major foundations associated with agriculture, I asked him what it would take to get the land-grant universities to change, to provide articulated co-operation between research and extension, among various disciplines, and between basic research specialists and other academics and extension personnel. The director's response, after several pulls on his pipe, was that it may already be too late to save the land-grant system. That was in 1978.

Johnson (1984) has revealed a counterproductive feature of agricultural academia that blocks attainment of what he considers the pre-eminent goals of the system. He contends that while the attainment of these goals requires an effective integration of problem-solving, subject matter and disciplinary types of research, the various 'chauvinisms' found on academic campuses inhibit the growth and development of the optimum balance of these three kinds of research.

For example, the philosophic chauvinism which posits the superiority of logical positivism is seen as the most damaging where it elevates the pursuit of hard-science 'positive' knowledge while denigrating as 'unscientific' the kinds of knowledge about human values that are crucial to problem definition. Somewhat less damaging, in Johnson's view, is the converse or 'normative chauvinism', which downplays the importance of hard-science positive knowledge while focusing on values and prescriptions of action to attain highly valued goals. Both forms of chauvinism are seen as 'anti-intellectual', running the risk of opening the door to 'mysticism and flights from knowledge' (p. 6).

Other forms of chauvinism that thwart the attainment of ultimate goals of agriculture are various disciplinary chauvinisms: the self-perceived superiority of one particular discipline inhibits interdisciplinary respect and therefore co-operation in addressing agricultural problems and opportunities.

Allied with the various disciplinary chauvinisms is what Johnson terms 'academic excellence as a chauvinism'. Increasingly, academic institutions are establishing elitist criteria of academic excellence which elevate intra-disciplinary research featuring innovative methodological and theoretical devices, while denigrating the more applied problem-solving and subject-matter types of research.

Schuh has observed that the land-grant system has lost its way (1984, 1986). Initially created as a response to the elitism and limited relevance of private universities in this country, the land-grant college system was intended to provide practical (what Johnson and Wittwer, 1984, call 'problem-solving') research and education, especially in agriculture and the mechanical arts. Gradually the commitment to problem-solving began to erode. Practicality began to be replaced with a disciplinary orientation. At many of the more prestigious institutions, applied work is now frowned upon, or at best tolerated, by those who bestow prestige and monetary rewards upon academics. Schuh observes:

> There is almost a perverse turning away from institutional responsibility. Professionals are self- and professional-peer oriented. They are concerned with advancing the state of knowledge and hence publishing for their professional peers, not generating and

applying knowledge for the solution of society's problems (p. 4).

> As a modern research university we want to be in on and contributing to knowledge on that frontier. And in my judgement we should be. The challenge is how to bridge that ever-widening gap between the frontier of knowledge and the problems the new knowledge we generate can ultimately solve . . . Basic research needs to be effectively articulated with the applied research (Schuh, 1984, p. 9).

Schuh contends that there is an abundance of research and educational work to do in dealing with the problems of society. Increasingly, private industry, community colleges and other institutions are usurping the roles formerly considered the exclusive domain of the land-grant institutions. Ominously he reasons: 'if we in the Land-Grant Universities really want to specialize in basic research and graduate training . . . If those are the things we want to limit ourselves to, then we need to be much smaller institutions'. Schuh goes on to predict that if we specialize ourselves into irrelevance, we can expect further reductions in political and financial support for our programs. He continues:

> But that is not my main concern. My main concern is what we will have sacrificed for society as a consequence of our growing irrelevance and the loss of effectiveness and payoff to society from its investment in the sciences and the arts (p. 23).

Commenting on the almost exclusive dedication to disciplinary interest, with professors catering to elites within their own professions, Schuh observes: 'the net effect of these developments is to effectively neuter university administrators. They would have a very difficult time developing a strong mission orientation even if they wanted to'. One of the research administrators interviewed for the Penn State study was bemoaning the lack of effective control or persuasive influence on professors. He said trying to influence the research agenda of a tenured full professor is a little like pushing on a string. And trying to influence a department is like pushing on a plate of spaghetti. Their reward system is oriented more toward their own discipline than toward the mission of the university as perceived by administrators. In the same view, Alpert (1985, p. 251) refers to the transfer of authority in academic matters from the president to the faculty as 'the academic revolution'. He contends that one result of this revolution has been a paralysis of academic institutions as related to better education, technological innovation, and rational well being.

The point of Schuh's analysis is not to argue that academics should cease the quest for scientific excellence and quality. Rather, he challenges the notion that publishing for one's disciplinary colleagues is the only – or even the most important – criterion for determining that quality and excellence. He challenges the institutions to find a way of revitalizing the land-grant sense of institutional mission, and to reward and encourage excellence in service to society as well as disciplinary excellence – and to accomplish all this without making dictators out of university administrators. He closes his essay as follows: 'It won't be easy to extricate ourselves from the box into which we have forced ourselves. But we owe it to both ourselves and the society of which we are a part to at least make the effort.'

Concurring with Schuh's central argument, Johnson (1984) contends that academia needs a 'new covenant', a dedication to attainment of super-ordinant societal goals, while setting aside our various chauvinisms, and seeking the most effective combination of disciplinary, problem-solving and subject-matter research. He calls for an increase in funding for all three types of research.

While a case could be made for an increase in funding for agricultural research of all three general types, in a time of budget austerity such as we seem to be entering, significant budget increases are highly unlikely. Past experience has demonstrated clearly that some organization and institutional strategies are much more effective than others in attaining agricultural goals. Rather than relying on larger budgets to finance more of all kinds of research, we may have to rely on better ways of organizing our research so as to achieve an institutional 'hybrid vigor'.

THE PERILS OF SUCCESS

In contemplating possible ways that academia might formulate a new covenant, one must be aware that there are dangers inherent in succeeding. Castle (1970, p. 839) observed a recurrent theme circa 1970:

> This is a notion that if the university could but (1) re-order their priorities and (2) organize properly to tackle 'real' social problems,

> rather than 'just increasing agricultural production', we would be off and running in our attempt to give rebirth to the land grant philosophy. As commendable as such an objective is, a word of caution must be raised. It is now clear that the success of the first land grant effort was largely in terms of first-round and direct effects, with other effects largely being ignored. *The social problems we are now addressing are, in large part, a manifestation of these indirect effects coming to the surface.* (emphasis added)

We have succeeded so well, for example, in increasing yields of various crops and dairy enterprises that the nation's warehouses are stuffed with surplus corn, wheat, cotton, dairy products and other price-supported commodities. The strong dollar, caused in large part by the massive federal budget deficit, has further suppressed domestic prices by undermining historically strong export markets. Meanwhile, back on the farm, some of the other indirect effects of our successes include environmental pollution by agricultural chemicals, the clogging of municipal water facilities and waterways by eroded soil, and hundreds of thousands of farmers on the verge of bankruptcy.

The classic example of a success going sour is the biologist who succeeded in transplanting the Gypsy Moth to these shores in the hope of creating a local silk industry; instead he created a monster that has denuded and killed millions of acres of forest. Chemists and entomologists who have succeeded in creating a powerful arsenal of pesticides have inadvertently visited upon mankind a veritable Pandora's box of lethal surprises just now beginning to be detected in our soils, water and foods. Federal policy-makers who succeeded in removing the great price fluctuations in major crops have inadvertently provided the income guarantees needed by farmers as collateral to finance the purchase of huge machines and vast blocks of land. *Ipso facto* they have sealed the fate of the moderate-scale family farm. Castle goes on to challenge the social sciences to work out how to treat these indirect effects successfully. I would add that it is not enough simply to treat the detrimental indirect effects of our 'successes'. Rather, we must develop our sciences to the point where we can anticipate and prevent detrimental impacts and thereby achieve a much greater benefit for society.

Spurred on by the Winrock report (Rockefeller Foundation, 1982), universities are clamoring to create biotechnology programs. Buttel

(1984, p. 137) observes that the products of biotechnology research can be extremely beneficial in substituting renewable for non-renewable resources, by coming up with high-yielding plant and animal species, genetic disease resistance, nitrogen fixation capabilities in non-leguminous crops, and other innovations not yet imagined. He warns, however, of the potential ecological and social impacts that could emerge, and he makes a plea for monitoring the development and diffusion of biotechnology. Buttel suggests in Chapter 8 of this book that developing countries can use this new technology, or may be victims of it.

CYCLES OF POLICY-MAKING

The creation of biotechnology institutes and a plethora of other such entities is an example of a policy-making philosophy which favors the creation of new organizational structures, rather than the modification or improvement of traditional ones. This kind of policy-making process is characterized in Figure 7.1. First, a 'great problem' is identified; the policy-maker decides this problem can and must be solved. The knee-jerk tendency of many policy-makers (especially those of a liberal persuasion) is immediately to create a 'new program' to solve the great problem. Familiar examples include the creation of a new nutrition education program, a rural development program, or a new regional research laboratory.

After a period of program operation, congressional oversight hearings are held to review the new program. Findings of the assessment are influenced by political pressure exerted through various interested organizations and individuals, by the administration's attitude toward a program, and sometimes by the results of scientific studies, including possibly an evaluation of the program. Depending on the outcome of the assessment, the program may receive accolades followed by more funds to continue or expand the program. In the case of disenchantment with the program, it will be either modified or terminated. In this case, if the great problem has been 'solved' or is no longer important to powerful interests, the policy-maker's attention is directed toward the identification of a new 'great problem', and so on.

This continuous cycle is also operative in academic institutions. In response to clientèle group or legislative mandates, university administrators may attempt to promote research to solve a particular

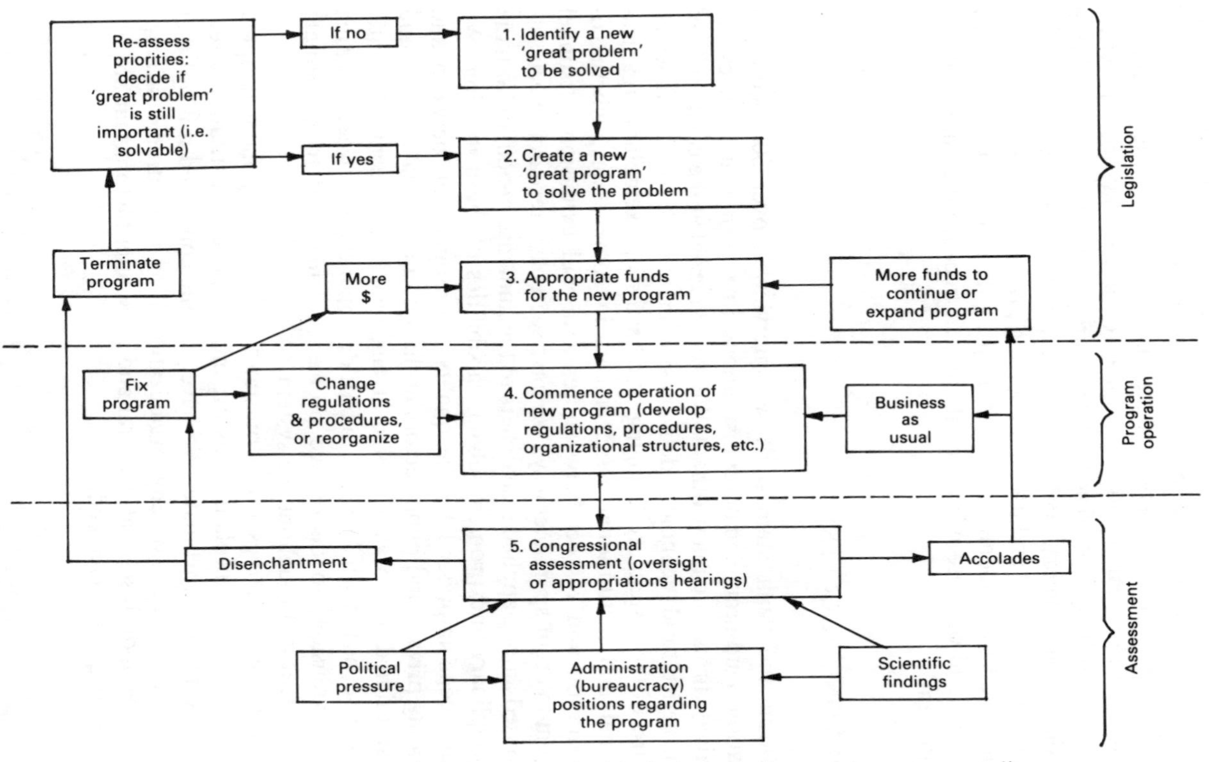

Figure 7.1 Cycles of policy-making: legislation, operation, assessment, recycling

problem or to enhance the institution's ability to cope with some specific type of problem. In this case, however, the ability of the institution to contribute to the solution of the problem may not be limited by a lack of knowledge, but by the focusing of faculty attention to research and educational resources away from practical problem-solving toward activities that are professionally rewarding in a disciplinary context. As Leontief (1971, p. 3) has observed, 'methods known to be valid and useful for solving practical problems are often laid aside by academics, and replaced by more esoteric (not to say more valid or more useful) methods . . . because they are new and different'.

BEYOND SUCCESS

During the Penn State study we interviewed over 300 people in various land-grant and other institutions, in government agencies and private firms, and many others. We were amazed at the complexity of the agricultural technology delivery system, and the speed with which parts of the system are changing. We have seen exemplary organizational and institutional arrangements in some states, where co-operation and respect between research and extension personnel seem to occur spontaneously. We have seen basic research specialists housed among applied researchers to the immense benefit of both the disciplinary and problem-solving capabilities of the institution. We have been impressed by the quality of co-operation between and among private and public actors in the system. We have also found institutional and organizational arrangements that seem inherently perverse, as though designed to block co-operation between research and extension, to discourage problem-solving, and to perpetuate separateness throughout the system.

When one observes a truly outstanding institution, one is tempted to advocate a transplant of its organizational and institutional features to the less fortunate. We have become convinced it is not that easy. The success of any organizational or institutional strategy depends upon historical, cultural and personnel factors that are not easily or quickly changed.

THE IMPERATIVE OF A NEW COVENANT

The survival and prosperity of agricultural academia requires that we adopt a new covenant, a commitment to be scientifically excellent, socially relevant, and ecologically responsible. The development of such a covenant is complicated by the rapidly changing roles of the public and private actors in the technology delivery system, as well as the constantly changing array of problems and opportunities facing agriculture and society as a whole. Difficult as the task may seem, however, it is imperative. The survival of agricultural academia demands it. Even more importantly, in the hard times that lie ahead, society will need the best we can offer. We can deliver our best only as we lay aside our chauvinisms, heal our separateness, and commit ourselves and our institutions to the solution of important problems and the attainment of worthwhile opportunities.

References

Alpert, Daniel (1985) 'Performance and Paralysis', *Journal of Higher Education*, 56: 241–79.

Bonnen, James T. (1983) 'Historical Sources of US Agricultural Productivity. Implications for R&D Policy and Social Sciences Research', *American Journal of Agricultural Economics*, 65: 958–66.

Busch, Lawrence and Lacy, William B. (1983) *Science, Agriculture and the Politics of Research* (Boulder, Colorado: Westview Press).

Buttel, Frederick H. (1984) 'Biotechnology and Agricultural Research Policy: Emergent Issues', Bulletin No. 140, Department of Rural Sociology, Cornell University, Ithaca, NY.

Castle, Emery N. (1970) 'Priorities in Agricultural Economics for the 1970's', *American Journal of Agricultural Economics*, 52: 831–40.

Castle, Emery N. (1981) 'How to Change Agricultural Research and Extension to Make it a Better Investment', in *Increasing Understanding of Public Problems and Policies – 1981* (Oak Brook, Ill.: Farm Foundation): 49–53.

Feller, Irwin, Kaltreider, Lynn, Madden, J. Patrick, Moore, Dan and Sims, Laura (1984) 'The Agricultural Technology Delivery System: A Study of the Transfer of Agricultural and Food-Related Technologies' (University Park, Penn.: Institute for Policy Research and Evaluation).

Hawken, Paul (1983) *The Next Economy* (New York: Holt, Rinehart & Winston).

Johnson, Glenn L. (1984) 'Academia Needs a New Covenant for Serving Agriculture', (Mississippi State: Mississippi Agricultural and Forestry Experiment Station Special Publication).

Johnson, Glen L. and Wittwer, Sylvan H. (1984) 'Agricultural Technology Until 2030: Prospects, Priorities & Policies', Special Report 12, Michigan State University, Agricultural Experiment Station, East Lansing, Michigan.

Kendrick, J. B. (1984) 'Agricultural Research is on Trial', *California Agriculture*, 38: 5–6.

Leontief, Wassily (1971) 'Theoretical Assumptions and Nonobserved Facts', *American Economic Review*, 61: 1–7.

Martin, Philip L. and Olmstead, Allen L. (1985) 'Agricultural Mechanization Controversy', *Science*, 227 (8 February): 601–6.

Rockefeller Foundation and Office of Science and Technology Policy (1981) *Science for Agriculture*, Report of a Workshop on Issues in American Agriculture (New York: The Rockefeller Foundation).

Schuh, G. Edward (1984) 'Revitalizing the Land Grant University', represented at a colloquium of the Strategic Management Research Center, University of Minnesota, St. Paul, Minnesota, 28 September.

Schuh, G. E. (1986) 'Revitalizing Land Grant Universities', *Choices*, 1: 6–10.

Splinter, W. E. (1980) 'Agricultural Mechanization: Who Wins? Who Loses?', *Agricultural Engineering*, 61(5): 14–17.

Strange, Marty (1984) 'Down on the Farm', NOVA TV program interview, first broadcast on 20 March.

8 Biotechnology and International Development: Prospects for Overcoming Dependence in the Information Age

Frederick H. Buttel and Martin Kenney

INTRODUCTION

The last ten years have been marked by protracted crisis in the global economic system. The economies of the less developed countries (LDCs) initially seemed immune to the stagnation that began in the early and mid-1970s in the developed countries. The 1970s were an era of intense growth for LDCs such as Brazil, Mexico, Korea and Taiwan – in substantial measure because formerly highly profitable areas of production were moved from developed countries to LDCs in search of cheap labor while simultaneously becoming lower profit industries. In retrospect we can now see that this phase of capital mobility was the root of a growth boom that, up to the end of the 1970s, buoyed the economies of many LDCs. By the end of the 1970s, however, the investment boom in the Third World had peaked. Even the relatively 'successful' LDCs that were the major beneficiaries of the global capital mobility of the 1970s became mired in the global recession, calling into question whether even the privileged handful of 'semi-industrialized' countries will be able to adopt successfully the heavy industry and consumer durables growth model that supported post-war economic expansion in the North.

Coincidentally, in the developed countries a new economic growth model had become increasingly discernible in the patterns of industrial investments in the 1970s and early 1980s. The key product of the high-technology industries associated with this model is information. These information technologies are providing the infrastructure to link developed and developing countries into an even more closely integrated global economy. In this New Information Age, LDC dependence on the developed world is being transformed. The roles of the various LDCs are becoming increasingly differentiated, and each country or group of countries is receiving a more specific insertion in the world economy (Fröbel, 1980). But despite the increasing diversity of LDCs and of their roles in the world economy, we argue that most LDCs could conceivably derive significant advantages from the New Information Age. This paper examines the newest and perhaps most powerful of all the new information technologies: biotechnology. Biotechnology is a very broad term which includes traditional techniques such as fermentation and plant breeding, and the new biotechniques, such as recombinant DNA, cell fusion, bioprobes and hybridoma-based antibody production. In keeping with current usage (see, for example, Office of Technology Assessment, 1981), more traditional 'biotechnologies' such as fermentation and plant breeding are omitted from the category of biotechnology throughout this paper unless specifically included.

We will briefly describe the world biotechnology industry and in so doing examine the barriers to transferring biotechnology to the LDCs. We will argue that despite the possibilities and continued availability of biotechnology to LDCs, many LDCs will likely be unable to reap biotechnology's benefits. Our inquiry is guided at a general level by concerns that have been raised in the literature on dependency (Amin, 1976; Frank, 1967, 1969), especially on technological dependency (Cardoso and Faletto, 1979; Evans, 1979; Becker, 1983; Gereffi, 1983), and by the 'post-dependency' response to criticisms of early formulations of dependency theory (Chilcote, 1981; de Janvry, 1981; Petras, 1983; Roxborough, 1979).

BIOTECHNOLOGY AND THE GLOBAL BIOTECHNOLOGY INDUSTRY

In 1973 recombinant DNA (later to be patented and therefore to become a commercial invention) was discovered by a Stanford University and a University of California, San Francisco, research team. This was a fundamental step forward: the DNA program of a cell could now be 'edited', 'rewritten' and inserted into a cell (a miniature 'factory' for protein production). After subsequent advances in molecular biology, biotechnology's potential applications in agriculture, health care, sanitation and energy soon became increasingly apparent as being of direct relevance to improving living standards in LDCs. Biotechnology now seems to be the newest buzz-word in the international development community, and there have already appeared numerous publications (e.g. National Academy of Sciences, 1982) that tout the potentials of biotechnology for the LDCs and make recommendations about research priorities for LDC biotechnology applications.

The world biotechnology industry can be divided into two distinct types of companies. The first type consists of small biotechnology start-ups that are usually less than ten years old and have only recently begun to manufacture products and generate a cash flow. The other type of company consists of large chemical, pharmaceutical, food processing, and oil multinational corporations (MNCs). The early technological leaders in biotechnology have been the small start-ups, which have been able to secure access to leading university researchers and to provide an environment conducive to technical innovation. The start-ups, however, lack capital, scale-up skills, marketing networks, and cash flow – the most important assets of the MNCs.

Whereas the start-up phenomenon is largely confined to the US and, to a lesser extent, the UK, the MNCs involved in biotechnology represent nearly all of the major industrial countries. The MNCs are pursuing various strategies to secure a foothold in biotechnology, including: (a) forming in-house research groups, (b) making investments in start-up companies, (c) letting research contracts to start-ups, and (d) forming relationships with universities. The last three strategies represent an attempt to secure access to university researchers or former university scientists who are now employed in start-up firms.

The MNCs are intent upon marketing the information and products they derive on a global basis, including the LDCs. But it is significant that despite the importance being attached to biotechnology by MNCs in developed countries, until recently very few LDCs have made a sustained effort to invest in biotechnology. The major exceptions thus far have been Brazil, Mexico, China, Cuba and India, with Thailand, Indonesia and the Philippines also having begun to make biotechnology investments. Clearly the intensive research effort underway in the developed countries, especially the US and Japan, makes it likely that attempts by LDCs to compete at the cutting edge of biological science and technology will be difficult.

Also, it is increasingly the case that the unfettered international flow of information which has characterized biomedical and agricultural science is being curtailed. One aspect of this truncation of the flow of scientific information is the recognition by developed-country firms, universities and university scientists of the value of biotechnological information. Another aspect is the orientation increasingly being expressed by governments of the world's leading biotechnology powers that they should not risk their lead in this major new technology, which some believe could be a locomotive to pull their economies out of recession and stagnation (see, for example, US Government Interagency Working Group, 1983). This restriction of information will also likely be manifest in agricultural research, a sector that is still largely characterized by public research funding and by an as yet remarkably free flow of information (Kenney and Buttel, 1985).

Although the trend has been toward restriction of the flow of information (or, at a minimum, to charge a fee for information), much useful biotechnical and agricultural information remains in the public domain. The ideology of scientific interchange and the 'world community of scientists' is a powerful force and has ensured that the channels of necessary scientific and technical information are not yet closed. Further, the start-ups, due to their pressing needs for capital infusions, are willing to sell know-how. And because LDCs will not be immediate competitors to the start-ups, LDCs can often extract favorable contract terms. The fact that many types of information will increasingly be made available only for a fee can and should be resisted by LDC governments, but it is also necessary for the LDCs to take advantage of the possibilities of purchasing needed information and capabilities while they are still for sale.

AGRICULTURE – ON THE VERGE OF THE BIOREVOLUTION

Agriculture was a major beneficiary of the previous accumulation model based on petrochemical inputs and mechanization, which increased agricultural productivity and contributed to the growth of trade in inputs and agricultural products. Such a large and important industry has until recently been only tangentially affected by the new information technologies. But with remarkable speed a new information technology – biotechnology – has been applied to agricultural

R&D. As we have noted elsewhere (Kenney and Buttel, 1985), agriculture – in both the developed and developing countries – will be profoundly transformed by the new biotechnologies.

It is useful to note that much of the dependency and post-dependency literature has placed major emphasis on the problems associated with the Green Revolution experience dating from the 1960s (see, for example, Galli, 1981; de Janvry, 1981; Roxborough, 1979). It has generally been observed that, in certain countries and regions, the agricultural productivity gains associated with the Green Revolution tended to come at a cost: increased inequality in the countryside and growing foreign exchange problems associated with importing petrochemical inputs from the MNCs of the developed countries. It is thus intriguing to speculate as to whether the emergent 'Biorevolution' will repeat the uneven performance of its predecessor, the Green Revolution. This is likely to be the case in many respects, especially in developing countries in which there remains a high degree of inequality in landholding systems and rural political structures. Nevertheless, in our research we have come to the view that there are likely to be substantial differences between the Green Revolution and the Biorevolution (Buttel *et al.*, 1985). Two such differences deserve particular emphasis. First, the Biorevolution promises to be of far broader applicability to LDC agriculture than was the Green Revolution; whereas the major thrust of the Green Revolution was confined to a handful of cereal grains in restricted geographical regions, the Biorevolution has the potential to affect virtually every agricultural species (including livestock as well as crops) and region. Second, the course of the Biorevolution, especially with regard to plant improvement, will be influenced to a far greater degree by proprietary considerations than was the Green Revolution.

Contemporary agriculture has increasingly been characterized by the use of purchased industrial inputs – for example, seeds, fertilizers, pesticides and fossil fuels. The manufacturers of these traditional chemical and genetic inputs, e.g. Monsanto, Ciba-Geigy, Sandoz, Dupont, largely hold the key to increased agricultural productivity in the coming age of biotechnology. This is particularly the case because over the past fifteen years, formerly independent US seed companies have increasingly been integrated into large MNCs (Butler and Marion, 1983; Buttel *et al.*, 1985), most of which are pursuing biotechnology R&D. Also, roughly two dozen of the start-up companies that have been formed in the US are emphasizing the development of superior varieties of crops, many of which are widely grown in LDCs.

One of the issues raised in the technological dependency and post-dependency literature (e.g. Evans, 1979; de Janvry, 1981) has been whether the technologies deriving from R&D in the advanced industrial countries will be appropriate for, or alternatively will result in distortions in, LDC economies. We also noted earlier that one of the crucial characteristics of the current development of biotechnologies is the dominance of private sector firms in R&D and the proprietary character of these technologies. Private firms in the advanced industrial countries that are developing these technologies have a clear interest in pursuing global markets for their products, including markets in LDCs. The R&D goals of these firms are thus largely market-driven; the technologies for which there are the largest potential markets will be given the highest priority, and prospective technologies with less attractive markets will tend to be overlooked. Thus while LDC markets for biotechnologies promise, in the aggregate, to be potentially quite attractive, the issue remains as to whether the technologies that are ultimately developed will be adequate to meet the needs of the rural and urban poor who possess little purchasing power.

Though no important biotechnological products for agriculture have been marketed in the LDCs as of the time of writing, some possible implications of the imperative of private firms to emphasize commercially valuable R&D can be illustrated by the research of a US biotechnology start-up, Calgene. Calgene has discovered and patented a resistance gene to Monsanto's Roundup, a herbicide which contributes over $500 million annually to Monsanto's gross revenues. Calgene has transferred the resistance gene to plant cells in vitro (Gebhart, 1984). These plant cells, and likely whole cotton and other crop plants, will then be able to tolerate larger doses of Roundup – an important discovery because many weeds have developed resistance to Roundup so that a given field requires much heavier doses of Roundup to remain weed-free. These larger doses of Roundup, in turn, have been toxic to some crop plants.

The significance of this type of research thrust lies, at the micro level, in the types of agriculturalists who will be in a position to use the technology and, at the macro level, in its impacts on the mix of inputs that will be employed in agricultural production. Since the goal of the research is not the reduction of pesticide usage, but rather to breed pesticide-tolerant plants so as to permit increased herbicide applications, it will be relatively affluent and well-capitalized producers who would be in the best position to benefit from herbicide-tolerant crops. Smallholding peasants with cash shortages and lack of access to credit would be less likely to use such a technology effectively. At the macro level, this type of research would shift the mix of resources employed in agriculture toward imported, capital-intensive inputs. Such a shift would also tend to increase the pressure on the already strained foreign exchange accounts of many Third World countries.

Biotechnology, however, is a technology with potentially broad applications. Biotechnology can be employed in ways that benefit the mass of the rural and urban poor or, alternatively, that provide even further advantage to privileged social classes. The choices to be made among alternative biotechnology R&D goals in agriculture may be especially crucial for LDCs. For example, instead of emphasizing the development of herbicide-tolerant crops, biotechnology research for LDC agriculture could quite conceivably be devoted to developing bacterial pesticides or allelopthic mechanisms implants in order to reduce the use of imported petrochemicals in agriculture. A similar dilemma will likely be manifest in the approach to plant improvement in LDC agriculture. It seems increasingly apparent that the new research tools that biotechnology represents are intensifying the emphasis of private firms on pursuing hybrids of major LDC crops such as wheat and rice. Hybridization, which renders crops reproductively unstable, will enable yield increases in wheat and rice but will compel wheat and rice farmers to enter the market each year to purchase seeds. Hybrids will enable private firms to incorporate proprietary genes (e.g. for herbicide or salt tolerance) and ensure that these genes are available to farmers only if they purchase seed each growing season. The biological protection of hybridization will thus complement the legal protection of plant breeder's rights, plant patents and trade secrets, thereby ensuring that private firms will be able to appropriate a return on their investments in biotechnology and plant breeding. The productivity improvements that will result in cereal grain production may make a significant contribution to feeding the malnourished populations of LDCs. But alternative biotechnological approaches may make possible equally impressive productivity increases without recourse to hybridization and reproductive instability of sexually propagated crop varieties. Reproductively stable, non-hybridized crop varieties would be more broadly accessible to the smallholding peasants of the developing countries, since farmers would be able to save their own seeds and reduce input costs in successive cropping seasons. At a national level, the minimization of seed and other input imports would benefit LDC economies.

BIOTECHNOLOGY: POSSIBILITIES FOR ESCAPING DEPENDENCE

It was indicated earlier that there is currently a great deal of enthusiasm among many development professionals concerning the promise of biotechnology for LDC development (see, for example, Dixon, 1983; Daly, 1983). In many respects we are in agreement with this view, for reasons that we will stress later in this section. However, the image of biotechnological panaceas for LDC development problems envisaged in many recent enthusiastic pronouncements deserves scrutiny. Most such observers have viewed LDCs and their populations as benefiting from various biotechnologies largely by becoming consumers of biotechnology products such as improved crop and animal varieties, new vaccines, and so on. We suggested earlier some theoretical and empirical reasons why developing countries merely becoming consumers of biotechnological products will likely do little to alleviate dependence. Moreover, given the fact that the LDCs' rural and urban poor tend not to constitute attractive markets for MNC biotechnology companies, it is not clear that biotechnological innovations will be rapidly diffused to LDCs through market mechanisms or, for that matter, that the biotechnologies most appropriate for the Third World poor will even be developed.

But while biotechnology will not automatically and painlessly solve the LDC development problems, it is important to emphasize that one of the most crucial aspects of biotechnology is that it is relatively inexpensive and thus potentially accessible to most developing nations. In 1980, N. Schneider (1980, p. 45) of E. F. Hutton estimated that a first-class genetic engineering facility would require 25 PhDs and $25 million for its first three years of operation. The capital investment required for biotechnology scale-up and production is five to ten times greater than research and is a necessary step in manufacturing products to meet human needs. But even full-scale biotechnology production facilities are not expensive when compared to facilities such as steel mills and oil refineries. For example, G. D. Searle's recombinant DNA pilot plant in the UK cost only $15 million and will be able to produce commercial quantities of products such as interferon (Kramer, 1981, p. 1).

Biotechnology is thus much less expensive than many previous industrial technologies and may be especially well suited to LDCs with little investment capital. Biotechnology may therefore be a technology from which Third World countries can benefit by becoming producers – and hence controllers of the research agenda – as well as consumers of the technology. But while biotechnology is relatively inexpensive and suitable for Third World countries to pursue with a significant degree of autonomy, substantial investments will be required, and these investments will need to be carefully targeted. These efforts, if well planned, can enhance Third World access to the new biotechnologies, maximize the benefits that can be gained through backward and forward linkages in the economy, and reduce the foreign exchange problems that have tended to plague Third World industrialization efforts over the past fifteen years.

BARRIERS TO APPLYING BIOTECHNOLOGY TO LDC PROBLEMS

The development of a viable indigenous biotechnology industry provides important opportunities to weaken the bonds of dependence by allowing LDCs to develop products uniquely suited to their needs. Infrastructural, economic and political barriers, however, could seriously retard indigenous biotechnology innovation.

Infrastructural obstacles, though in most cases expressions of enduring socioeconomic problems (including the legacies of dependence and distorted development) are the most easily resolvable through technical fixes. For example, an efficient research establishment of any type requires uninterrupted services such as electricity, telephone service and water. Also important are adequate transportation links to an international airport to ensure timely access to research materials such as enzymes and maintenance services for research equipment. Another important infrastructural consideration is the availability of trained personnel. Virtually all LDCs have suffered serious drains of trained scientists and engineers. The lack of other trained personnel, such as competent technicians, computer programmers, and so on, can seriously hamper access to international information networks. But these staff problems are not intractable and can be solved through a combination of sending technicians overseas for training, improving systems of higher education, and making compensation and facilities attractive for scientists and other trained personnel.

An important and perhaps crucial obstacle may be access to biotechnological information. LDC libraries are notoriously underfunded, and periodicals typically arrive late, if at all. The costs of securing information are substantial, especially given the importance in biotechnology of building and maintaining information retrieval networks through access to on-line data bases.

In any LDC the cost of a development project is an important concern, especially when significant amounts of foreign exchange will be expended for imports of necessary capital and research inputs. It should be noted, of course, that biotechnology investments are negligible by comparison with the costs of imported military hardware, pesticides and pharmaceuticals. Yet the scientific instrumentation necessary for biotechnology R&D does require significant initial investments: for example, a fully outfitted pilot fermentation plant would cost nearly $4 million, depending upon the type of fermentor purchased, and an electron microscope would cost between $100 000 and $200 000. Nevertheless, the fact remains that biotechnology is economically outside the grasp of only the smallest and poorest countries, and even these countries could form regional research consortia through which to develop their own biotechnology research programs and production facilities.

At the economic level what is often the most constraining factor in LDC development planning is the lack of markets for the products of new industries such as biotechnology. Scientists and private firms, in both the developed and developing countries, have tended to deemphasize applied research oriented toward the needs of the Third World poor because of the lack of markets for products. Thus, private firms in the LDCs are likely to be constrained as much by the lack of robust internal markets in developing countries as are their counterparts in the developed countries. For this reason, there will probably be few LDC firms that make biotechnology investments, especially in products that will be accessible to the rural and urban poor. LDC governments are therefore more likely than the LDC private sectors to invest in biotechnology. Indeed, for many LDCs the most viable option for the eventual commercialization of biotechnology products may be to establish state corporations for R&D, scale-up, production and marketing. Biotechnology commercialization through state corporations would have important advantages over private sector commercialization, even if the enterprise were eventually transferred to private ownership. First, retention of biotechnology operations in the state sector would preserve public input into the research agenda and may increase the probability that there would be R&D devoted to socially valuable projects for which there is limited market demand. Second, the state sector has a greater ability to absorb short-term losses, to assume a longer planning horizon, and to subsidize privately unprofitable but socially valuable activities.

A further and perhaps fundamental obstacle to developing an effective indigenous biotechnology capacity in LDCs relates to the lack of political will on the part of Third World leaders. On one level, starting a biotechnology program is far more complex than purchasing a 'turn-key' steel or chemical factory; a biotechnology program requires a long-term planning effort detailing the manner in which research resources should be deployed and identifying promising projects with realistic goals. Biotechnology may thus not be highly attractive to LDC political and economic elites with a preference for risk-free, high-visibility investments with a short pay-off period. At another level, ruling regimes may be tightly linked to multinational firms or otherwise owe their positions to dominant classes at home or abroad. Biotechnology programs that would potentially provide competition to the product lines of major foreign (or domestic) firms thus may be viewed less than enthusiastically by the political elites of many LDCs.

CONCLUSION

Dependence cannot be transformed and eliminated by biotechnology any more than any technical fix can provide 'development'. But biotechnology does offer unique – perhaps unprecendented – opportunities to raise standards of living and the quality of life in LDCs that have the political will and social structures to adapt and diffuse biotechnological innovations. Conversely, the advance of biotechnology elsewhere in the world economy may well represent a vehicle for deepening dependence and distorted development. Any country that simply opens itself up to the 'benefits' of exogenously produced biotechnology inputs, such as the ones that will soon be on the world market, will likely encounter one or more of the following situations.

Some small, poor LDCs will remain untouched by biotechnology because they do not represent attractive markets for MNCs. Other countries experiencing significant biotechnology market penetration will find themselves more dependent than ever due to the increased outflows of hard currency to pay for biotechnology products. Still other countries will find their own chemical, pharmaceutical and other industries outcompeted by MNCs which employ new biotechnological techniques.

Biotechnology thus serves to heighten what has for some time been the basic dilemma of peripheral development: cheap labor versus expansion of the domestic market as motors of capital accumulation and economic growth. Failure to achieve autonomous biotechnology industries may well exacerbate the problems of narrow markets, balance-of-payments constraints, and technological dependence. But biotechnology is perhaps better suited than any previous major industrial technology to enabling Third World countries to mitigate dependence and embrace domestic-market-led economic development. The mid-1980s will be a pivotal period in this regard, since the private and public decisions being made right now will have a major influence on the course of Third World development decades into the future.

References

Amin, S. (1976) *Unequal Development* (New York: Monthly Review Press).

Becker, D. G. (1983) *The New Bourgeoisie and the Limits of Dependency* (Princeton, N.J.: Princeton University Press).

Butler, L. J. and Marion, B. W. (1983) 'An Economic Evaluation of the Plant Variety Protection Act', unpublished manuscript, Department of Agricultural Economics, University of Wisconsin-Madison.

Buttel, F. H., Kenney, M., and Kloppenburg, J. Jr (1985) 'From Green Revolution to Biorevolution: Some Observations on the Changing Technological Bases of Economic Transformation in the Third World', in F. H. Buttel *et al.* (eds) *Economic Development and Cultural Change*, forthcoming.

Cardoso, F. H. and Faletto, E. (1979) *Dependency and Development in Latin America* (Berkeley and Los Angeles: University of California Press).

Chilcote, R. H. (1981) *Theories of Comparative Politics* (Boulder, Col.: Westview Press).

Daly, J. (1983) 'Biotechnology: Accelerating Development', *Horizons*, 2 (November): 18–21.

Dixon, B. (1983) 'The Third World's Greatest Opportunities', *Bio/Technology* (August): 494, 519.

Evans, P. (1979) *Dependent Development* (Princeton, NJ: Princeton University Press).
Frank, A. G. (1967) *Capitalism and Underdevelopment in Latin America* (New York: Monthly Review Press).
Frank, A. G. (1969) *Latin America: Underdevelopment or Revolution?* (New York: Monthly Review Press).
Fröbel, F. (1980) *The Current Development of the World Economy* (Tokyo: United Nations University).
Galli, R. (ed.) (1981) *The Political Economy of Rural Development* (Albany: State University of New York Press).
Gebhart, F. (1984) 'Calgene Researchers Clone Gene for Herbicide Resistance', *Genetic Engineering News*, 4 (January/February): 25.
Gereffi, G. (1983) *The Pharmaceutical Industry and Dependency in the Third World* (Princeton, NJ: Princeton University Press).
Janvry, A. de (1981) *The Agrarian Question and Reformism in Latin America* (Baltimore: Johns Hopkins University Press).
Kenney, M. and Buttel, F. H. (1985) 'Biotechnology: Prospects and Dilemmas for Third World Development', *Development and Change*, January: 61–92.
Kramer, N. (1981) 'Lilly Plants Progressing', *Genetic Engineering News*, 1 (July/August): 1, 12.
National Academy of Sciences, National Research Council (1982) *Priorities in Biotechnology Research for International Development* (Washington, DC: National Academy Press).
Office of Technology Assessment (1981) *Impacts of Applied Genetics* (Washington, DC: Office of Technology Assessment).
Petras, J. (1983) 'New Perspectives on Imperialism and Social Classes in the Periphery', in P. Limqueco and B. McFarlane (eds) *Neo-Marxist Theories of Development* (London: Croom Helm): 198–220.
Roxborough, I. (1979) *Theories of Underdevelopment* (London: Macmillan).
Schneider, N. (1980) 'Prepared Statement of Nelson Schneider at a Hearing before the Subcommittee on Science, Technology and Space of the Committee on Commerce, Science and Transportation, US Senate', in *Industrial Applications of Recombinant DNA Techniques* (Washington, DC: US Government Printing Office).
US Government Interagency Working Group on Competitive and Transfer Aspects of Biotechnology (1983) *Biobusiness World Data Base* (New York: McGraw-Hill).

Author Index

Alpert, Daniel, 107
Amin, S., 120
Anderson, R., 79
Armsby, Henry, 26
Atwater, Wilbur, 26

Baer, Michael, 90
Bain, Ian, 50
Baker, Gladys, 26
Barickman, Nancy, 50
Battenfield, S., 63
Becker, D., 120
Berry, Jeffrey, 89
Berry, Wendell, 26
Bezdicek, D., 63
Black, John, 26
Boehlje, Michael, 50
Bonnen, James, 107
Bowers, William, 27
Brass, P., 79
Briggs, Harold, 50
Brown, L., 63
Browne, William, 89
Buchanan, R., 27
Busch, Lawrence, 27, 79, 107
Butler, L., 120
Buttel, Frederick, 63, 64, 107, 120, 123

Cardoso, F., 120
Castle, Emery, 107
Chilcote, R., 120
Cochrane, W., 63
Cummings, R., Jr., 80

Dahlgren, R., 63
Dalrymple, D., 79
Dalsted, Norman, 50
Daly, J., 120
Danbom, David, 27
Dishman, William, 90
Dixon, B., 121
Duda, A., 63

Edens, T., 63
Eidman, Vernon, 50
Elliot, L., 63
Emerson, Carolyn, 50
Emley, W., 29
Evans, P., 121
Evenson, R., 79
Ezekiel, Mordecai, 27

Faletto, E., 120
Feller, Irwin, 107
Fitzharris, J., 80
Frank, A., 121
Fridgen, C., 63
Friedland, William, 27
Friley, Charles, 27
Frobel, F., 121

Gais, Thomas, 89
Gajbhiye, H., 79
Galli, R., 121
Gates, Paul, 27
Gebhart, F., 121
Gee, Wilson, 27
George, S., 80
Gereffi, G., 121
Guither, Harold, 89

Hadwiger, Don, 27, 79, 80, 89
Hardin, Charles, 89
Hartford, C., 27
Hawken, Paul, 107
Henkes, R., 63
Herrick, H., 27
Hightower, Jim, 27
Hildreth, R., 80
Holmberg, M., 63
Hughes, R., 27
Hurt, R., 27

Janvry, A. de, 120
Johnson, Glenn, 107
Johnson, R., 63

Kaltreider, Lynn, 107
Kappel, Tim, 27
Keeney, D., 63
Keller, Evelyn, 27
Kendrick, J., 108
Kenney, M., 120, 121
Kessler, K., 63
Kile, Orville, 27
Kirkendall, Richard, 27
Kislev, Yoav, 50
Kloppenburg, J., Jr., 120
Knapp, Joseph, 28
Knight, H., 27
Knoblauch, H., 27
Kohl, D., 63
Koppel, B., 80
Kramer, N., 121

Lacy, William, 27, 79, 107
Law, E., 27
Lee, Harold, 27
Leontief, Wassily, 108
Levy, E., 79
Lockeretz, W., 63
Lowi, Theodore, 90
Lukens, J., 63
Lush, Jay, 28
Lusk, Graham, 28

McCalla, Alex, 28, 90
McCollum, E., 28
McWilliams, Carey, 28
Madden, J. Patrick, 107
Marcus, Alan, 28
Marion, B., 120
Marti, Donald, 28
Martin, Philip, 108
Meyer, Neil, 90
Meyer, W., 27
Milbrath, Lester, 90
Moore, Dan, 107
Morrison, B., 79
Myrick, Herbert, 28

Nevins, Allen, 28
Nordin, Dennis, 28
Nourse, Edwin, 28
Nugent, J., 51

Olmstead, Allen, 108
Olson, Mancur, 90
Oram, P., 80

Papendick, R., 63
Parr, J., 63
Paulson, Jo Ann, 50
Peffer, E. Louise, 28
Persons, Stow, 28
Peterson, Mark, 89
Peterson, Willis, 50, 80
Petras, J., 121
Power, J., 63

Rainsford, George, 28
Raup, Philip, 50
Richards, Henry, 28
Risser, J., 63
Rosenberg, Charles, 28
Ross, Earl, 28
Rossiter, Margaret, 28
Rowe, Harold, 29
Roxborough, I., 121
Ruttan, Vernon, 13, 29, 51, 80

Sachs, C., 79
Salisbury, Robert, 90
Schneider, M., 121
Schuh, G. Edward, 108
Scott, Roy, 29
Shapiro, Henry, 29
Shearer, G., 63
Sims, Laura, 107
Skolnikoff, E., 80
Smith, Edward, 51
Smith, Howard, 29
Splinter, W., 108
Strange, Marty, 108
Sweeney, O., 29
Swoboda, R., 63

Terpenning, Walter, 29
True, Alfred, 29
Truman, David, 90

Vance, Rupert, 30
Vogeler, Ingolf, 30

Waksman, Selman, 30
Walker, Jack, 89, 90
Ward, John, 30
Williams, James, 30
Wilson, James, 90
Wiser, Vivian, 30
Wittwer, Sylvan, 107
Wolf, E., 63
Woodruff, H. Boyd, 30
Wortman, S., 80
Wright, M., 63

Yotopoulos, P., 51
Youngberg, I., 63, 64

Zeigler, L. Harmon, 90

Subject Index

academe, agricultural, 93
adversity, 5
agricultural academe, 93
Agricultural Experiment Act, 20
agricultural research, 1
Agricultural Research Service, 24
agricultural sector, 5
agricultural technology, 53
alternative farming, 53
American agriculture, 33
assessment, 105

biorevolution, 112
biotechnology, 109
bonanza farms, 35

centers, research, 11
change, technical, 35
constituents, 15
cooperation, 12
cycles, 104

debt-asset ratio, 41
declining support, 5
developing nations, 11
development, international, 109
dissent, 94
distribution, technology, 12
distributive policy, 7
DNA, 110

ecological damage, 10

Farm Bureau federation, 83
farming, alternative, 53
farm management, 42
farm size, 35
farm structure, 56

genetic engineering, 116
global biotechnology, 110
Green Revolution, 113
group structure, 6

high input agriculture, 9
history, 15
herbicides, 114

inefficiency, 33
infrastructure, 8
information age, 109
international development, 109
international research, 11

Land Grant Act, 16
land-grant system, 72
LDC problems, 117
legislation, 105
less-developed countries, 109
loan policy, 43
loan rate, 43

management, farm, 42
mixed blessing, 93
monocultural agriculture, 9
multinational corporations, 111

National Grange, 22
new covenant, 93

operation, 105
organic farming, 53

perils of success, 102
policy environment, 7
policy-making, 104
policy setting, 1
public research, 11

R&D investment, 98
recycling, 105
redistributive policy, 7
research alternatives, 31
research benefits, 11
research centers, 11

research corporations, 11
research institutions, 15
Rural Coalition, 86

size, farm, 35
social damage, 10
structural adjustment, 33
structure, group, 6
success, 102
support, declining, 5

technical change, 35
technology distribution, 12
Third World development, 120
time of adversity, 5

USDA, 17